Dramascr

Dicing with Death

THREE MEDIEVAL PLAYS

15

Nelson

Thomas Nelson & Sons Ltd
Nelson House
Mayfield Road
Walton-on-Thames
Surrey KT12 5PL
United Kingdom

Designed and produced by Bender Richardson White
Typesetting by Malcolm Smythe
Cover illustration by Dave Grimwood
Black and white illustrations by John James
Printed by L. Rex Printing Co. Ltd., China

This edition published by Thomas Nelson & Sons Ltd 1999
ISBN 0–17–432596–7
9 8 7 6 5 4 3 2
03   02   91   00   99

CONTENTS

SERIES EDITOR'S INTRODUCTION

Dramascripts is an exciting series of plays especially chosen for students in the lower and middle years of secondary school. The titles range from the best in modern writing to adaptations of classic texts such as *A Christmas Carol* and *Silas Marner*.

Dramascripts can be read or acted purely for the enjoyment and stimulation that they provide; however, each play in the series also offers all the support that pupils need in working with the text in the classroom:

- **Introduction** – this offers important background information and explains something about the ways in which the plays came to be written.
- **Script** – this is clearly set out in ways that make the plays easy to handle in the classroom.
- **Notes** explain references that pupils might not understand, and language points that are not obvious.
- **Activities** – at the end of scenes, acts or sections – give pupils the opportunity to explore the plays more fully. Types of activity include: discussion, writing, hot-seating, improvisation, acting, freeze-framing, story-boarding and artwork.
- **Looking Back at the Plays** – this section has further activities for more extended work on the plays with emphasis on characters, plots, themes and language.

DICING WITH DEATH: INTRODUCTION

The plays in this anthology are based upon three of the greatest stories in medieval English literature.

The Pardoner's Tale, on which the title play, *Dicing with Death* is based, is one of the most popular episodes in *The Canterbury Tales*, written by Geoffrey Chaucer in the last few decades of the 14th Century. The painful account of Judas's betrayal of Jesus forms the basis for the second play which recreates a series of rehearsals for one of those great dramatic achievements of the Middle Ages, the mystery plays. *Sir Gawain and the Green Knight*, composed by a contemporary of Chaucer's whose identity is still uncertain, is among the strangest of all stories to be inspired by the legends of King Arthur and the Knights of the Round Table. In each of the dramas there are characters who, in one sense or another, are dicing with death.

Individually these plays offer new perspectives on three early classics of early English literature and drama. Taken together, they embody the most fundamental hopes, fears and beliefs of the people who lived and worked in medieval England, as well as giving evidence of the enduring and unique power of drama in recreating stories which enable us to make sense of our existence.

Dramascripts

Dicing with Death

An adaptation of Geoffrey Chaucer's
The Pardoner's Tale

Simon Adorian

INTRODUCTION

Dicing with Death is based on *The Pardoner's Tale,* one of *The Canterbury Tales* written by Geoffrey Chaucer between 1387 and 1400. In *The Canterbury Tales* a group of pilgrims collect in an inn in London and prepare to travel to a holy shrine at Canterbury Cathedral. They agree to shorten the journey (by horse and on foot) by telling one another stories along the way. The whole work is about 17,000 lines long and is mainly written in rhyming verse. *The Pardoner's Tale* is just one of the 24 tales which Chaucer completed. It is a tale with a moral which exists in a number of versions in different countries.

Before telling his tale, the Pardoner admits that he is a priest who earns his living by selling fake relics and pardons to simple folk who buy them to avoid being sent to Hell when they die. To understand the story fully, you need to remember that medieval England was a deeply religious society. Although few people could read or write, everyone went to church and was familiar with the Bible. Heaven and Hell featured in stories, sermons and paintings of the time; death was never far from people's minds. Plague epidemics swept across Europe in the 1300s; the worst of these, known as the Black Death, wiped out at least a quarter of the population of Europe in 1349.

Simon Adorian's dramatisation of the story begins with a group of travelling actors preparing to perform. Like the Pardoner in Chaucer's poem, they admit that their main reason for presenting this story is that it will strike fear into the audience and persuade spectators to hand over their money. The performers are confident that they have a story whose humour, violence and chilling moral would strike a chord with any audience . . .

THE CHARACTERS

GROUP OF TRAVELLING PLAYERS (at least five)

HARRY (the leader)

WALLY (the largest) } three wild, young rioters

JAKE (the smallest)

COFFIN BEARERS (four)

SERVANT

LANDLORD

THE OLD MAN

APOTHECARY

CITIZEN IN THE STREET

CROWD IN THE TAVERN

PROLOGUE

A group of PLAYERS are setting up a stage, unpacking props and costumes. One of them is looking into a large purse.

PLAYER 1	Here – how much've we got in the kitty?	1
PLAYER 2	Not a lot. Count it yourself. *(Throws the purse back to PLAYER 1 who opens it up and carries out a brief count.)*	
PLAYER 2	Well?	
PLAYER 1	Six pence, a button . . . and a tooth.	
PLAYER 2	Huh?	
PLAYER 3	Times are hard.	
PLAYER 4	Getting harder.	
PLAYER 3	And unless we make some cash soon, there'll only be one thing for it.	10
PLAYER 4	*(Horrified.)* You don't mean . . . ?	
PLAYER 2	Surely not?	
PLAYER 3	Yes. We'll have to get ourselves proper jobs. Labouring with our hands.	
PLAYER 2	Working the land, making baskets, ugh.	
PLAYER 4	But I'm too sensitive to wield a spade. My creativity will be stifled.	
PLAYER 3	Never mind your creativity, it's the blisters I'm worried about.	

 kitty *A pool of money into which everyone makes a contribution.*

(Long pause. PLAYERS sit on stage dejectedly.)   20

PLAYER 1   So? We've seen worse than this. Come on, my friends, lift your heads. There's a big audience out there. We'll show them a story to free up their purses. We could make enough today to keep us in wine and women for the next month.

(He has a good look at the audience.)

PLAYER 5   They don't look very . . . well . . . bright.

PLAYER 3   Or rich. They smell dreadful.

PLAYER 1   No matter. These simple crowds often yield the richest pickings. Remember your craft. You know the best ways to part an audience from its money.   30

PLAYER 4   A sword fight.

PLAYER 5   Die well. It always works.

PLAYER 3   Send out the smallest one with the begging bowl.

(They give the bowl to the smallest PLAYER.)

PLAYER 1   Don't forget the look.

(The small PLAYER puts on the most pathetic, appealing face he/she can and holds out the bowl.)

PLAYER 2   Or the limp.

(Small PLAYER drags a leg as if bravely suffering intense pain.)

PLAYER 1   Better still, we'll put the fear of God into them with a   40
religious text. Let's go for the one that never fails.

ALL   *Dicing with Death!*

PLAYER 2   That'll put the wind up them.

PLAYER 1   Bumpkins like this lot love it. A good, old-fashioned morality tale. Always has them fishing for their purses.

(PLAYERS quickly set up the main props, find costumes and take up their positions. They set up a tavern scene around a table at

which HARRY, WALLY and JAKE are playing at dice. In the
background, are the LANDLORD and a CROWD of other
drinkers.)   50

(Two PLAYERS hang a banner across the main stage area which
reads, The Love Of Money Is The Root Of All Evil. *The small*
PLAYER takes the begging bowl out into the audience.)

(One PLAYER takes centre stage and coughs loudly.)

PLAYER   Ladies and gentlemen,
                  Our aim today will be to entertain,
                  But also to improve, to teach, to train.
                  We know you would not want a play be shown
                  Unless it was of high and moral tone.
                  And if you're pleased by our morality,   60
                  Feel free to show your generosity.

(Small PLAYER shakes the begging bowl determinedly at
someone in the audience.)

                  Our tale begins with these three drunken guys
                  Who liked to haunt the shadiest of dives,
                  Three riotous youths steeped in sinfulness,
                  Wasting their lives in wretched drunkenness,
                  Their money spent on ale and dicing,
                  Blaspheming, partying, womanising.
                  Their habits foul, their language fouler still,   70
                  To hear them swear would make your blood run chill.
                  The more they drank, the cussing just got worse,
                  If nothing else, these boys knew how to curse.

The love of money is the root of all evil *A biblical quotation from a*
letter from St Paul. This can be found in the New Testament (reference
1 Timothy 6.10).

blaspheming *Talking in a way which insults religion, e.g. using the name*
of God to swear.

cussing *Swearing.*

The moral that our tale will demonstrate
Is one good folk like you appreciate.
For the sake of those that cannot read,
We say the greatest sin of all is greed.
(Small PLAYER rattles the bowl.)
The love of money is a sad business,
It only ever brings unhappiness.   80
(Small PLAYER rattles the bowl even louder.)

Take these three drunkards in the inn . . .
See how they earned the wages of their sins!
Their dreadful fate will show you all too well
How gambling took them down the road to Hell,
Till raising the stakes with every breath
They found themselves dicing with death!

*(PLAYER bows to the audience and points towards the tavern
scene which comes alive.)*

DISCUSSION In this scene the players know that their play has to be successful or they will go without food. They talk about *'the best ways to part an audience from its money'*. Modern producers of films and plays also have to think about pulling in the crowds.

Draw up a list of ingredients for a modern-day box office success.

ARTWORK Read the stage direction on page 7 where the players set up their stage. They hang up a banner showing the moral of the play – *'The Love Of Money Is The Root Of All Evil'*.

Look at examples of decorated medieval texts and design a version of this banner.

RECITE THE POEM Prepare a recital of the introduction to the play which is written in verse. You will need to think about:
- bringing out the patterns of rhyme and rhythm.
- the moral message of the poem (even though the character of the player might not believe in it!).

If working in a group, you could use different voices and add music to create more of an impact.

SCENE 1

HARRY	Where can he have got to? God's teeth – do we have to wait any longer to get this game under way?	1
WALLY	No worries, Harry. He'll be along later. He promised me.	
JAKE	Start without him. Just the three of us. We'll fleece him later, like we always do. He's got more money than sense, he has.	
HARRY	Pull up a chair for him.	
	(JAKE fetches a chair and they make a fourth place at the table and start the game.)	
WALLY	What're we playing, Hal?	10
HARRY	A game of Hazard. You boys both in? Jake? Wally?	
JAKE & WALLY	*(Putting coins on the table.)* We're in.	
HARRY	Jake. You be caster.	
	(JAKE throws the dice. The CROWD all cheer and shout out the number thrown.)	
CROWD	Seven!	
JAKE	Main roll of seven. Cast your bets now – if you dare!	
HARRY	*(He slams some coins on the table.)* Raise you five!	
WALLY	*(Puts down coins.)* Make it ten!	

God's teeth *See* blaspheming *above. It was common in the Middle Ages for people to swear on God's bones, teeth and nails – the body parts which were often kept as holy relics from the bodies of Christian martyrs.*

fleece *To trick out of money, to 'rip off'.*

Hazard *An ancient gambling game played with two dice.*

HARRY	Suits me. Jake to throw. Seven or 11 to win.	20

WALLY *(Shouts.)* More wine! More wine! Come on, shift your arse!

JAKE *(Cupping the dice.)* Come on, lucky seven, lucky seven, lucky seven. Come on my beauties. *(Throws.)* Yeah!

(JAKE leaps around the table, dancing, shouting and punching the air in celebration.)

CROWD Seven! Seven wins it! Jake! Jake! Jake!

(HARRY leaps across the table, pins JAKE against the wall and draws a dagger.)

HARRY By God's nails, if you've played me false, you'll pay for this.

WALLY Easy, Harry. The boy won fair and square. Put the blade away.　　　　　　　30

HARRY I'm just warning him, that's all. 'Cos if he ever does cheat me, he'll feel this dagger between his ribs. *(He puts the dagger away.)*

JAKE Ease up, Harry – no need to be in such a strop. What you want is a drink. Have one on me. *(Shouts.)* In fact, everyone – the drinks are on me!

(The CROWD cheers. HARRY, WALLY and JAKE settle back to the table and pour drinks.)

WALLY This is the life, hey?　　　　　　　40

(Solemn music and slow drumbeat. The CROWD falls silent. Four COFFIN BEARERS walk past the stage, carrying a coffin.)

HARRY Oy!

COFFIN BEARER Sir?

HARRY Who've you got in there, then?

COFFIN BEARER Perhaps you would know, if you had not spent your day dicing.

JAKE Watch your tongue, man. We'll have you know we haven't just spent our day dicing. We've been drinking as well!

(WALLY breaks wind loudly.)   50

WALLY   Better out than in.

HARRY & JAKE   *(Fanning the air around their noses.)* Urgggh, Wally!

WALLY   Sorry, boys.

HARRY   Listen, pal, just tell us who you're burying. We don't need any advice on how to live from you with your face as long as a wet Sunday.

COFFIN BEARER   It looks as if you are in need of plenty of advice. As the Book tells us, *The wages of sin is death.* Once there were four dicers, now there are but three. *(To the other COFFIN BEARERS.)* Move on.   60

(Funeral procession leaves, drum beating slowly.)

 The wages of sin is death *Another quotation from a letter of St Paul.* (Romans 6.23)

11

(HARRY, WALLY and JAKE stare at the empty chair in stunned silence.)

HARRY   It must have been . . .

JAKE   No wonder he was late for the game.

WALLY   And he owed me money.

HARRY   Shut up! This is no joking matter.

WALLY & JAKE   Sorry, Haz.

HARRY   We've got to do something to avenge our mate.

WALLY & JAKE   Revenge!   70

HARRY   But first, we gotta find out who it was who killed him.

WALLY & JAKE   Ah! Good plan, good plan.

HARRY   You boy!

(SERVANT comes over to the table.)

HARRY   Were you aware of this . . . er . . . inconvenience to our business partner?

SERVANT   The whole village has talked about nothing else for the past day, sir.

(WALLY collapses face down on the table. JAKE puts a bottle to his mouth.)   80

HARRY   So how come we didn't know?

(SERVANT looks at the table where WALLY is snoring and JAKE is slurping loudly.)

SERVANT   I can't imagine, sir.

JAKE   (Leaping up and staggering around the stage.) So who killed him? 'Cos, whoever it is, he'd better watch out! Just give us his name.

(Long pause. WALLY snores on.)

SERVANT	His name . . .	
HARRY & JAKE	Yes?	90
SERVANT	. . . is Death.	

(WALLY wakes with a start. HARRY and JAKE look alarmed.)

SERVANT   A sly thief, he is. Broke into your mate's house in the dead of night and caught 'im in his sleep, just as 'e was, drunk as a skunk, so 'e never knew a thing about it. Stole up on 'im and stabbed 'im through the heart.

WALLY   The dirty, lowlife scumbag!

SERVANT   He's a dangerous customer, make no mistake. During this recent plague, he must've done away with a thousand folk round these parts. You want to be on your guard against this Death bloke.   100

(LANDLORD comes over.)

LANDLORD   The boy's right, I tell you. You should see what this Death has done in the next town, only a couple of miles from here.

JAKE   What's that, then?

LANDLORD   Only gone and killed every man, woman, child and serf in the place, that's all. I wouldn't be surprised if he wasn't still out that way. But he's not someone you'd want to meet.

HARRY   You reckon? You think we're scared?   110

JAKE   Us? Scared of Death? Huh! We're hard, we are.

WALLY   Rock hard.

 serf *A peasant slave belonging to the estate of a rich medieval landowner.*

HARRY	I'll go through the town street by street till I catch up with him.
JAKE	Me too.
WALLY	And me.
HARRY	And I swear by God's bones, we'll track him down and then we'll have him.
WALLY & JAKE	Yeah!
HARRY	Listen, boys. Wally, Jake, hold up your hands and swear 120 we're in this together, and together we'll kill this traitor Death who's done in so many of our countrymen. Yes?
WALLY & JAKE	We swear.
WALLY	Just let us find him and he's dead!
JAKE	Death is dead!
	(HARRY, WALLY and JAKE arm themselves with whatever is available – a broomstick, dustbin lid, clubs, etc. As they do so, they take up JAKE's chant. They start to leave.)
HARRY, WALLY & JAKE	Death is dead!
LANDLORD	One moment, gentlemen. Your bill? 130
HARRY	You talk of the bill at a time like this? We're off on a heroic quest to slay the evil foe Death and you quibble over a few measly pence on the slate?
LANDLORD	But, but . . .
WALLY	Shame on you, sir.

 on the slate *On account, to be paid for at a later time.*

JAKE	Petty, money-grubbing cheapskate!
HARRY	Out of our way! We'll settle up with you when we return. But first we have a score to settle with Death!
	(The CROWD cheers and HARRY, WALLY and JAKE set off, chanting as they go.)
HARRY, WALLY & JAKE	Death is dead! Death is dead! Death is dead! 140

IMPROVISATION Devise a scene in the tavern just after the departure of Harry, Wally and Jake. The parish constable arrives having received complaints of rowdy behaviour in the tavern and interviews the landlord, the servant and other drinkers.

LANGUAGE STUDY Look again at page 14 (from *'I'll go through the town street by street'* to *'Just let us find him and he's dead'*). Now read these lines from Chaucer's *The Pardoner's Tale*, written in the 14th Century:

'Ye, goddes armes!' quod this riotour,
'Is it swich peril with hym for to meet?
I shal hym seke by wey and eke by strete,
I make avow to Goddes digne bones!
Herkneth, felawes, we thre been al ones;
Lat ech of us holde up his hand til oother,
And ech of us bicomen othere brother,
And we wol sleen this false traytour Deeth.
He shal be slayn, he that so many sleeth,
By Goddes dignitee, er it be nyght!'

The Chaucer wording is hard to read because the English language has changed over time.

- How many changes in spelling and vocabulary can you find?
- List words which have stayed the same.

SCENE 2

A track on the way to the town.

	(We hear HARRY, WALLY and JAKE chanting Death is dead! before they march in. Already they look more dishevelled.)	
HARRY	Left, right, left, right.	1
	(An OLD MAN appears wrapped in a black cloak so that only his skull-like face can be seen. Sinister music announces his entrance. As they approach him, the three rioters go quiet.)	
HARRY	And . . . halt!	
	(WALLY and JAKE stop clumsily.)	
OLD MAN	Good-day, gentlemen.	
HARRY	Good-day, my arse! Get out of our way, you . . . old person.	
OLD MAN	Certainly, gentlemen.	
HARRY	*(Mimicking.)* 'Certainly, gentlemen. Certainly, gentlemen.' Eurggh! You make us sick, you do.	10
WALLY	Just answer us this question, will you?	
OLD MAN	I'll do my best, sir.	
	(HARRY and JAKE snigger. They continue to mimic.)	
WALLY	Why are you so old? Eh? Old person.	
OLD MAN	My answer to you is simply this: although I have wandered far and wide across the world, through village and town, I have yet to find anyone who would swap their youth for my age.	
HARRY	Huh! I'm not surprised. Look at the state of you. I'd hate to be that old.	20

OLD MAN	You will be – but only if you're lucky. And this is how I shall remain until God wills it. Until then, not even Death will come for me and I'm condemned to eke out this miserable old life, waiting, waiting for Death.
	But as for you, hasn't anyone taught you to show a bit of respect to the older generation?
	(HARRY, WALLY and JAKE jeer at him.)
OLD MAN	Anyway, I must press on . . .
HARRY	*(Barring the OLD MAN's way with a stick.)* Not so fast, old guy. We've not finished with you yet.
OLD MAN	What could you possibly want with me?
HARRY	Just now you mentioned someone.
JAKE	Someone we've got business with.
WALLY	Death.
HARRY	The filthy traitor lives round about these parts. You spoke of him just now – I suppose you're in league with him.
JAKE	You look like him – on a bad day at that!
OLD MAN	Listen, if you're so keen to come face to face with Death.
HARRY, WALLY & JAKE	Which we are.
OLD MAN	Just follow this path and keep going till you reach that oak tree over there. Can you see it? I left him there only a few minutes ago.
HARRY, WALLY & JAKE	Yes! *(Chanting.)* Death is dead! Death is dead!
	(HARRY, WALLY and JAKE charge off, leaving the OLD MAN looking after them.)

30

40

OLD MAN   God speed you on your way. And may you find everything that you deserve.

(Sinister music. Fade to blackout.)

TAPE THE SCENE The Old Man is a mysterious and sinister figure. His costume, the way he speaks and background music will all help to build up his sense of mystery. Prepare a taped version of this scene, using some musical effects.

Try to contrast the quick pace of the three rioters with the slow delivery of the Old Man.

SCENE 3

By the large oak tree. Underneath the tree lies a big sack. We hear HARRY, WALLY and JAKE approaching, still chanting. As they come near to the sack, HARRY puts a finger to his lips and points to the sack. The others go quiet. They all clearly think that the sack is a sleeping body and they make signs to organise a clumsy ambush. They creep up on the sack, showing varying levels of bravery. HARRY and WALLY push JAKE forward, giving him a knife to stab the sack.

JAKE pounces and wrestles with the sack long after it is obvious that it is not a person. Some gold coins roll out on to the floor and HARRY and WALLY scrabble for them. JAKE remains clutching the sack.

HARRY & WALLY	Gold!	1
JAKE	I'm rich!	
HARRY & WALLY	*(Moving menacingly towards JAKE until he releases the sack.)* We're rich.	
HARRY	Listen, guys. This calls for some quick thinking and I'm clearly the man for it. Lady Fortune's smiled on us today all right – just look how much dosh we've got here. But we need a plan.	
WALLY	Why?	
HARRY	Because we've got to get the gold away from here. We've got to find a way, without anyone seeing us, of carting it off to my place.	10
WALLY & JAKE	Your place?	
HARRY	And yours too, obviously. What I mean is, we can't do it by day or people will see us and then they might think we'd nicked it.	
WALLY	As if!	
WALLY & JAKE	Hell's bells!	

(WALLY and JAKE drop the coins they were holding and move sharply away from the sack.) **20**

HARRY So . . . we've got to work under cover of darkness. Here's the plan. We draw lots and whoever gets the short straw legs it into town for bread and wine. Meanwhile the others guard the treasure till it's dark. Is it a deal?

WALLY & JAKE It's a deal, Harry.

HARRY *(Quickly prepares lots and they draw. JAKE draws the short straw.)* Jake! You win again!

JAKE Huh?

(HARRY gives him two coins from the sack.)

HARRY Here's some cash. Off you go, then. Bread and wine. Yes? **30**

JAKE Bread and wine.

HARRY And not a word to anyone.

JAKE Not a word.

HARRY See you soon. Byeee!

(JAKE runs off. WALLY waves after him.)

WALLY Bye bye, Jake. And remember not to tell anyone about the treas . . .

(HARRY claps a hand over WALLY's mouth.)

HARRY Shut up, you idiot! All you've got to do is shut up and guard this stuff until it's dark. Have you got that? **40**

WALLY I've got it, Harry. *(He sits down by the sack and promptly falls asleep. HARRY paces, clearly hatching up a plan.)*

HARRY Er, Wally?

WALLY *(Waking.)* Yeh?

HARRY You know how you're my best mate, don't you?

WALLY *(Puzzled.)* Yeh?

HARRY	Well, I've been thinking.
WALLY	Oh.
HARRY	Thinking about all this lovely treasure, Wally.
WALLY	Oh yes.

50

HARRY	Thinking how much treasure we've got to split three ways.
WALLY	Mmmm.
HARRY	Thinking how much more we'd get if we were to split it two ways, between the two of us, between you and me, Wally.
WALLY	Oh, but we can't do that. You see, Jake knows we've got the treasure and what would he say?
HARRY	Well, that depends, doesn't it? I mean, what if something were to happen to our little friend? Like a bit of an accident, if you catch my drift.
WALLY	Oh yeah, you can count me in. Never did like him much.

60

HARRY	Right. The two of us can easily sort him out. When he gets back with the booze, you pick a scrap with him.
WALLY	What? Fight him?
HARRY	Only a play fight. Just mucking about between mates. Then, when you've got him in a hold, I'll creep up behind him and stab him in the back. Then you draw your dagger and get him as well and then all the money's ours and all our problems are over for ever and we can spend the rest of our days drinking and dicing! Nice plan, hey?
WALLY	Very nice plan.

70

 DISCUSSION AND WRITING This scene ends with Harry's cunning plan. At this point there are many possible endings. In a group, brainstorm some storylines for the rest of this tale. Devise endings which fit in with this genre of morality tale.

SCENE 4

In the town. JAKE is ambling along a street, carrying a flagon of wine and a loaf of bread. He stops a passing CITIZEN.

JAKE	Excuse me.	1
CITIZEN	Yes?	
JAKE	I'm looking for an apothecary. Someone who really knows their stuff.	
CITIZEN	Oh dear. Not feeling well?	
	(JAKE holds his head and pretends to be ill.)	
JAKE	Just a little under the weather. I expect I'll pull through. Probably something in the wine.	
CITIZEN	Well, you take care of yourself. And if it's a good apothecary you want, just go over there at the sign of the lizard. He's your man.	10
	(CITIZEN leaves and JAKE goes over to the APOTHECARY's shop.)	
JAKE	Ah, good Mr Apothecary, just the man I need to help me.	
APOTHECARY	Oh yes? Are you wanting medicine?	
JAKE	Not as such, no. It's more poison that I'm after.	
APOTHECARY	Poison, sir?	

flagon *A large bottle with a handle.*

apothecary *Chemist.*

at the sign of the lizard *Before most people could read, shops or offices would use pictorial signs (like pub signs today). Houses in streets were not numbered, so these were used as addresses. For example, this apothecary's address would be 'At the sign of the lizard'.*

JAKE Yes, I've got a bit of a problem with some vermin that I need to wipe out. An infestation of rats, and also a stinking polecat that's hanging round the hens in my yard. I'd like to get rid of these pests before they clean me out.   20

APOTHECARY *(Pouring poison into a small container.)* I see. This'll do the trick. There isn't a creature alive that would survive a drop of this stuff.

JAKE That's what I like to hear.

APOTHECARY You won't find a deadlier poison than this.

JAKE *(Slams down a coin on the counter and picks up the poison.)* I'll take it. And you can keep the change.

APOTHECARY Oh, sir. You're too kind.

JAKE *(As he leaves.)* I know, I know. Too kind. *(He carefully pours*   30
the poison into the flagon.) Too kind for my own good. That's what I say, too damn kind.

FREEZE-FRAME Create a freeze-frame of Jake as he leaves the shop with the flagon of poisoned wine. Use different voices to speak out his private thoughts, plans, hopes and fears.

SCENE 5

By the oak tree. HARRY is counting out the coins into two piles. WALLY is keeping watch.

HARRY	And one for you, and one for me.	1

WALLY   Pssst. He's coming! He's coming!

(HARRY jumps up. He and WALLY try not to look suspicious, whistling. JAKE enters jauntily.)

JAKE   *(Like a waiter.)* Gentlemen, your groceries are delivered. Bread. Wine. I trust they will be to your liking.

(JAKE bends over to set down the bread and wine. As he does so, WALLY creeps up behind him and kicks his backside. JAKE spins round and WALLY has his fists raised.)

WALLY   Come on then.   10

JAKE   You what?

(WALLY tries, unsuccessfully, to look tough and slaps JAKE across the face.)

WALLY   Come on, then. I challenge you.

JAKE   Challenge me? You wouldn't challenge me if I had both hands tied behind my back, you great lump of lard.

WALLY   No, really. I want to fight you. Just a bit of fun. Come on, short-arse.

JAKE   Right, that's it!

(JAKE leaps at WALLY who screams in terror and tries to run away. JAKE is too quick and in no time has him in a grip. WALLY screams out in pain.)   20

WALLY   No, please. Ow, that really hurts, you know.

(HARRY creeps up behind JAKE and stabs him.)

HARRY	Die.
	(JAKE staggers and calls out in agony.)
JAKE	I thought I could . . . trust you.
HARRY	More fool you. It looks like we've won this game after all – and you were supposed to be the lucky one.
	(JAKE falls by the sack of coins and dies. WALLY whimpers and looks appalled.)
WALLY	He's dead. Isn't he?
HARRY	Yup.
WALLY	Oh, Harry, what've we done?
	(HARRY picks up the flagon and offers it to WALLY.)
HARRY	Don't be such a wimp. Get this down your neck.
WALLY	*(Swigging from the flagon.)* Thanks, Hal. We did it, didn't we? The gold's all ours now.
HARRY	*(Snatching the flagon and taking a swig.)* All ours, old chap. Every single penny.
	(HARRY and WALLY clutch their necks, look at one another in terror and slump to the ground by the sack.)

30

40

50

(Sinister music. Slowly, the OLD MAN approaches. He places a coin in each of the dead men's eyes, picks up the sack and leaves.)

(Fade to blackout.)

IMPROVISATION Improvise a scene in which some strangers discover the bodies of Harry, Wally and Jake.
- How would they react?
- What might they think has happened?

PERFORMING *Dicing with Death* ends with plenty of action (the fight, the poisonings, the visit of the Old Man). All this would need careful choreography.

Prepare a presentation of the ending, so that all the different actions are shown clearly. One way to do this would be to create a series of freeze-frames, with one line from the script for each frame.

WRITING Write brief notes to help actors playing the main parts of Harry, Wally and Jake. Describe each of these characters and give suggestions about their personalities, appearance, mannerisms, etc. Think about the ways in which comic actors use facial expressions, gesture and movement to take on a role.

SET DESIGN The action of *Dicing with Death* takes place in a number of different places, inside and outside.

Draw up plans for a simple set with important props so that all the different scenes can be set up quickly.

WRITING *Dicing with Death* is based on an ancient tale with a clear moral message about the evils of greed.

Write a contemporary story which would convey the same moral.

WRITING The play opens with a Prologue in which you see the players setting up and planning the entertainment.

Write an Epilogue (a closing scene) in which the players take down the stage, discuss how the performance went and count their takings. Set it out as a playscript, using stage directions.

Dramascripts

Mystery Play

A meeting and three days' acting

John O'Connor

INTRODUCTION

Mystery plays (sometimes called 'miracle plays') were an extremely popular form of drama for several centuries, lasting from the early Middle Ages to Shakespeare's lifetime.

The stories acted out were taken almost entirely from the Bible and were performed by working people who belonged to craft guilds (the word 'mystery' being from the Middle English *mistere*, meaning *a craft*). Each guild would take responsibility for a particular episode from the Bible, in many cases choosing a story which was appropriate to their particular craft. For example, the bakers might act out the Last Supper, the shipwrights Noah's Flood and the nail-makers the Crucifixion.

Although the performers were not 'professional' in the truest sense – they did not act for a living – some were paid for taking part, and the company would ensure that a skilled author wrote the script and that no expense would be spared in making costumes and props.

Once ready, the plays would be performed on 'pageant wagons' (elaborate stages fixed to carts) and audiences would wait at pre-arranged venues around the town, ready to see each company arrive on its wagon, perform its play and then move on, to be replaced by the next one.

A complete 'cycle' of plays might start with God's creation of the world, move through stories such as Cain's murder of Abel, and finish up with Judgement Day. There must have been mystery cycles all over England in the Middle Ages, but the best known today are the York, Chester, Coventry and Wakefield (or Townley) cycles.

Jesus, Judas and the Last Supper

One of the most powerful stories in the Christian Bible tells of Jesus's betrayal by one his followers (or 'disciples'), Judas Iscariot. This is the episode that the characters in our play are rehearsing, since, as the Baker's Guild, they would be the natural company to perform the story of the Last Supper (Jesus's final meal with the disciples), around which Judas's betrayal revolves.

The episode begins at the point where Judas, the disciples' treasurer, goes to the high priests and Pontius Pilate (the Roman Governor) to make a deal. Knowing that the priests and the Romans see Jesus's popularity as a threat to their authority, Judas promises that, in return for 30 pieces of silver, he will take them to Jesus, so that they can arrest him. The bargain is struck and Judas returns to the disciples who are celebrating the feast of Passover (see page 45). To show that the disciples must be prepared to serve others, Jesus washes their feet and then, beginning the meal, predicts that one of them will betray him, offering Judas a piece of bread as he speaks. The next scene takes place in the garden of Gethsemane, where Jesus is praying, fully aware that he will soon be arrested and crucified. Judas arrives, indicates to the Romans who his master is by kissing him, and Jesus is taken away.

But as soon as Judas realises what he has done, he is filled with remorse and tries to return the money. The high priests aren't interested, and, steeped in guilt, Judas hangs himself.

You can find the story in the four Gospels of Mark (chapter 14), Matthew (26–27 – the one who tells of Judas's death), Luke (22) and John (13–18).

THE CHARACTERS

THE BAKERS' GUILD PLAY COMPANY	*Parts in the* MYSTERY PLAY
RICHARD the company treasurer	*Judas*
GEOFFREY the script-writer	*Jesus*
ALYSON the costume-mistress	
GERVASE	*the disciple Peter*
ROBIN a new apprentice	*the disciple Andrew*
MARION the prompt; Geoffrey's mother	
SYMKIN	*Pontius Pilate*
KATHERINE the props-mistress	
OSWALD	*Annas, a priest*
HUBERT	*Cayaphas, the high priest*
ALEYN	*the disciple Thomas*

Non-speaking (disciples and soldiers in the mystery play)

HARRY

NICHOLAS

HODGE

JANKIN

MARTIN

ROGER

CHRISTOPHER

HENRY

The play can be performed on a bare stage.

It should begin and end with music, which also fades in and out – coordinated with the lighting – to cover scene-changes.

SCENE 1

It is early morning, May 1290. As the lights come up on a bare space, which might be a farm-yard or village green, a cock crows.

RICHARD enters, a rather shifty-looking young man, carrying a chest, which he sets down on the floor. Looking over his shoulder, he takes out a key and opens the lid. First he removes a heavy-looking book, some kind of accounts ledger, which he places on the ground beside him. Then, glancing around once more, he carefully removes several small bags from the chest and selects one by its weight which he stuffs furtively into his jacket.

He throws the other bags back into the chest, followed by the book, then slams the lid shut once more and turns the key in the lock. As he replaces the key round his neck, ALYSON enters, her arms full of theatrical costumes, with GEOFFREY, who is carrying some papers.

Glancing at RICHARD as she passes, ALYSON goes out, struggling under the weight of the costumes. GEOFFREY drops his papers on to the chest and smiles at RICHARD.

GEOFFREY	Checking the company's savings?	1
RICHARD	Yes. Just making sure everything's in order.	
GEOFFREY	Good. Where are the others?	
RICHARD	Collecting props and things . . . Getting some drink, too, I think.	
GEOFFREY	Very wise. Thirsty work.	

furtively Secretively and perhaps guiltily; Alyson spots what he is doing and later uses the same word (page 37).

(He laughs, looking at RICHARD, who, feeling more relaxed, joins in.)

RICHARD   Is it the same script as last year?

GEOFFREY   Almost. I've just rewritten a few sections – some of your   10
part, funnily enough.

RICHARD   My part?

GEOFFREY   Yes. Watching it last summer, it didn't seem to me that
Judas had reason enough for what he did, so I've added
some more 'motivation', as we call it in the trade.

RICHARD   Surely he does it for the money?

GEOFFREY   Oh, yes. Thirty pieces of silver must have been a great
temptation. But I felt – watching you acting the part – that
there was something else . . . Something personal.

RICHARD   In the way I acted it?   20

GEOFFREY   Yes. Something between the lines.

*(Before RICHARD can answer, GERVASE comes in, typically in a
bad temper, clutching a poster.)*

GERVASE   Here! Have you seen this?

GEOFFREY   The poster? Yes. Why?

GERVASE   I thought we were getting top-billing this year? We're tenth!
We're even below the water-carriers! I mean – the water-
carriers, for God's sake!

motivation *The term actors use for the reason a character has for doing
something.*

between the lines *Geoffrey spotted something in the way Richard had
acted it, something not in the script.*

getting top-billing *Getting our names at the top of the poster (as the
'star' act).*

GEOFFREY	They've simply listed the companies in the order of their plays. Look. The water-carriers are above us because they do *John the Baptist*. The nail-makers are after us . . .
GERVASE	. . . because they do the crucifixion, I know that. But we were told it wouldn't be listed that way this year.
	(ALYSON enters with a fisherman's costume. As she talks, she puts it on GERVASE for a fitting and adds pins here and there.)
ALYSON	Well it is, so keep your temper for once and swallow your pride. And stand still.
GERVASE	I am not proud! It is simply – Ouch!
ALYSON	Sorry.
GERVASE	. . . Simply – OUCH!
ALYSON	I am sorry – it's these pins.
GERVASE	Simply a question of professional etiquette.
ALYSON	You're not professionals – you're skilled amateurs.
GERVASE	Geoffrey gets paid for writing it, doesn't he? And we take a collection, don't we? Talking of which, Richard, how much have we saved from last year?

30

40

John the Baptist *The preacher who baptised Jesus in the River Jordan (an appropriate story for the water-carriers).*

a fisherman's costume Gervase is playing Peter, who had been a fisherman before becoming a disciple.

professional etiquette *The correct rules of behaviour, appropriate to the profession of acting.*

professionals . . . amateurs *Alyson is distinguishing between people who act for a living and those who perform plays for enjoyment (while still being very good at it).*

take a collection *The company would ask audiences to make voluntary contributions of money to watch the play.*

RICHARD	Actually, I haven't quite got the accounts up to date. I've just collected the chest, as a matter of fact. I was going to sort it out after the rehearsal.
ALYSON	Well, we'd better have enough. We've really gone to town on the costumes this year.
GEOFFREY	*(Smiling at RICHARD.)* We'll have enough, I'm sure.
	(Some of the others enter noisily, carrying their scripts, bits and pieces of costume – the Roman helmets are especially noticeable – and odd props, such as wooden swords, goblets and a basketful of bread. ROBIN carries a long bench, HODGE and SYMKIN a trestle table between them.)
ROBIN	Here we are, master!
GEOFFREY	Thank you, Robin. Excited?
ROBIN	*(Nods.)* First time. Am I really playing Andrew?
GEOFFREY	If you want to.
ROBIN	I want to.
GEOFFREY	*(Handing him his script.)* Good.
	(MARION and KATHERINE enter with more costumes, assisted by ALEYN and HUBERT, and start to give them out to the various actors, calling them either by their real names, or by the parts they will play: 'SYMKIN!' 'Pontius Pilate!', 'Where's the high priest?' and so on. As the actors begin to try on their costumes, GEOFFREY gives out the rest of the scripts, calling the actors' names and assigning their parts.)
	Gervase! – Peter . . . Aleyn – will you do Thomas this year?
ALEYN	If it doesn't have too many lines.
GEOFFREY	You'll cope. Oswald and Hubert?
OSWALD	Annas, I trust . . .
HUBERT	. . . and Cayaphas?

50

60

70

ROBIN	*(Whispers to MARION.)* Who are Annas and – the other one?
MARION	Annas and Cayaphas: the high priests that Judas has dealings with. They're the ones who want Jesus arrested. Don't you ever listen in church?
GEOFFREY	Nicholas – you're a disciple again; Symkin – Pilate.
SYMKIN	Excellent.
KATHERINE	Why you're always Pilate, I can't imagine!
SYMKIN	Because I'm big and loud and swagger a lot, that's why!
	(There is general laughter at this, except from RICHARD, who is sitting anxiously waiting for his part.)
GEOFFREY	Harry, Hodge, Jankin, Martin, Roger and Christopher – disciples doubling as Roman soldiers as last year . . . *(They all go away with their scripts, looking pleased.)* Oh, and Richard?
RICHARD	Yes.
GEOFFREY	I'll give you the Judas script, but it still needs some attention – I'm not sure that it works as it is. I'll take it back after we've rehearsed for a few days if that's all right.
RICHARD	*(Slightly puzzled.)* Of course.
ROBIN	*(To MARION.)* Does the master always play Jesus?
MARION	He has done for the last five years. He's offered to let someone else do it, but no one seems to want to take it off him.
ROBIN	It's a responsibility, I suppose.
MARION	I think that's how he sees it, yes.

80

90

100

Because I'm big and loud . . . *Parts such as Pilate and Herod were famous for being played as loud, swaggering, over-the-top characters.*

GEOFFREY	*(Calling them together.)* All right, everybody, gather round for a moment, will you?
	(They assemble around him, some half in costume. KATHERINE and ALYSON carry on pinning and snipping while he talks.)
	As you know, we're making a special effort this year because of the rival cycle being planned in the city.
GERVASE	Pirates! Plagiarists! *(Struggling for words.)* . . . Copy-cats!
GEOFFREY	Thank you, Gervase. The fact is, though, that, since we were all given official permission to perform plays on Corpus Christi Day, cycles have been springing up all over the place. Ours wasn't the first and it certainly won't be the last. But we can make sure that it stays the best.
SYMKIN	Hear, hear!
	(They all join in with encouraging shouts until GEOFFREY calls them to order once more.)
GEOFFREY	Which means no one is late for rehearsals this year, Symkin . . .
SYMKIN	It was the sheep.
GEOFFREY	. . . no one goes fishing, Hodge . . .
HODGE	I had a cold, honest.
GEOFFREY	. . . and we all know our lines by the dress rehearsal, Oswald.

110

120

cycle *The whole series of plays, performed one after the other (see the Introduction, page 28).*

Plagiarists! *People who steal other people's ideas or creations and pass them off as their own.*

Corpus Christi Day *This was the important religious festival in July on which mystery plays could take place, according to an official ruling from the Church.*

OSWALD	I just forgot a character's name, that's all.
GEOFFREY	It was Jesus, Oswald, Jesus.

(Much laughter at OSWALD's expense.)

Today's meeting is really just so that you can take your parts home and look through them – we'll start rehearsals in earnest tomorrow. Most of you know your parts from last summer but there are two newcomers – Robin and Harry – and Aleyn will be taking a speaking part this year: he's playing Thomas.   130

(A few mocking 'Oohs!'.)

Also I'm thinking of changing one or two things in the Judas part, but I want to hear it through before I make up my mind about that. So, if there are no questions, we can finish early for today, but I'll expect to see you all after work tomorrow.

(A few people stay behind to work on props and costumes. As the others say their farewells for the day, GEOFFREY walks to one side and is joined by ALYSON.)   140

ALYSON	Geoffrey, can I have a word?
GEOFFREY	Of course. What is it?
ALYSON	Did you see? When we arrived?
GEOFFREY	See what?
ALYSON	Richard!
GEOFFREY	I saw him checking the padlock on the chest.
ALYSON	Furtively. He was checking it furtively.
GEOFFREY	Why should he do it furtively? He's the company treasurer – it's his business to make sure nobody's been tampering with it. 150
ALYSON	I still say it looked suspicious. Anyway, I don't like him,

Geoffrey. He's shifty.

GEOFFREY   You can't hang a man for looking shifty, Alyson.

(The tension is broken by a noise from the crowd.)

KATHERINE   Alyson! Come and give me a hand with Pilate, will you?

ALYSON   *(Over her shoulder, to KATHERINE.)* Coming! *(Then, quietly.)*
Watch him, Geoffrey.

*(She moves back into the crowd, which has now become quite
noisy, leaving GEOFFREY sitting thoughtfully on the chest as the   160
lights dim.)*

 ARTWORK Imagine you were making a film of this play. Storyboard
the opening stage directions, showing four key frames. The first frame
might look like this:

Sounds are of
a cockerel and
general farm-
yard noises.

The camera view
is constant until
the chest lid is
lifted; the view then
focuses on Richard's
worried face.

DISCUSSION Geoffrey must know that Richard isn't honest. Discuss why he
doesn't throw him out of the company.

SCENE 2

Day one of rehearsals. The lights go up on a busy scene: some are finishing getting into costume, some trying out actions (GERVASE swipes his sword rather dangerously), some practising their lines and checking difficult bits with each other.

GEOFFREY enters and, without any other greeting, he leaps on to the chest and, in a powerful voice, announces the opening scene of their play.

GEOFFREY	The Honourable Guild of Bakers presents the story of the capture of Jesus and his betrayal at the hands of the treacherous disciple Judas Iscariot. Scene one: Pilate's palace!	1
	(HODGE brings on a throne and places it centre-stage. Then SYMKIN, HUBERT and OSWALD enter, as PILATE, CAYAPHAS and ANNAS. As this is happening, MARION helps ROBIN with the background to the story.)	
MARION	Our play, you see, starts with Judas – the disciple who is planning to betray Jesus . . .	10
ROBIN	I know that much, Marion . . .	
MARION	. . . Just checking . . . Judas going to see the priests and Pilate, the Roman Governor. The priests want Jesus out of the way because he's a threat to their authority, and Pilate –	
GEOFFREY	Sssh!	
	(MARION mouths a 'Sorry' and they fall silent as the scene begins. Throughout the rehearsal sequences, the actors perform in a very professional and accomplished way. Some keep their scripts in their hands, but others – especially those who have played their parts before – deliver their lines from memory.)	20

a threat to their authority *See the Introduction (page 28).*

accomplished *Highly skilled; expert; extremely proficient.*

(As PILATE sits imperiously on his throne, CAYAPHAS on one side, ANNAS on the other, RICHARD enters as JUDAS, and kneels before him.)

JUDAS	Lord Pilate, all powerful, before you I kneel. If it's Jesus you're seeking, I'll offer a deal: Thirty pieces of silver is my bargain today . . .
PILATE	You lead me to Jesus and gladly I'll pay.
CAYAPHAS	But how shall we ken him, this 'King of the Jews'?
ANNAS	Amongst his disciples, which chap do we choose?
JUDAS	The one that you want won't be easy to miss: You must go for the man that I greet with a kiss.
PILATE	You'd better be faithful and make good your claim.
JUDAS	Trust me . . . as Judas Iscariot's my name.

30

GEOFFREY   Stop a moment. That's good, but, Richard, you're sounding too obviously villainous with that last line. Remember that Pilate has to trust you, so say it in a way that will make him believe you. Try it again. Give your cue-line, Pilate.

PILATE	You'd better be faithful and make good your claim.
JUDAS	*(This time saying it a little less like an obvious villain.)* Trust me . . . as Judas Iscariot's my name.

40

GEOFFREY   Nearly there. I'm still not quite believing you, though, Richard. Forget Symkin for a moment. Say the line to me. *(Pause.)* And make me believe you.

(RICHARD turns to GEOFFREY and, clearly finding it painful, looks him in the eye and utters the line with total sincerity.)

---

imperiously *Like an emperor; used to being obeyed.*

ken *A word used in some regional dialects for 'know'.*

cue-line *The final line of an actor's speech, which 'cues in' the next speaker.*

JUDAS	Trust me . . . as Judas Iscariot's my name.	

(There is a silence as they look at each other. When GEOFFREY speaks, it is very quietly.)

GEOFFREY	Good. Do you see the difference?	
RICHARD	Yes.	50
GEOFFREY	*(Louder.)* Take a short break, please, while I make a note.	

(GEOFFREY sits on the chest, front stage, making notes, as the others discuss what they have just done, have a drink or complain to ALYSON about their costumes. After a few seconds GERVASE detaches himself from the crowd and sidles over.)

GERVASE	Psst!	
GEOFFREY	I'm sorry?	
GERVASE	I said 'Psst'!	
GEOFFREY	Oh.	
GERVASE	I don't trust him, Geoffrey.	60
GEOFFREY	Who?	
GERVASE	Richard.	
GEOFFREY	Ah. Any reason, or just because he looks shifty?	
GERVASE	So you've noticed too? He does, doesn't he? But it's more than that. I saw him in The Red Lion, talking to Dickon – that baker in Longwall Street.	
GEOFFREY	Nothing strange in that, Gervase, they're both bakers after all. Probably bemoaning the price of wheat-flour.	
GERVASE	You don't keep looking over your shoulder if you're talking about the price of wheat-flour. And there's more.	70
GEOFFREY	Yeast?	
GERVASE	I'm serious, Geoffrey. Dickon's one of the writers for the city mysteries.	

GEOFFREY	I know.
GERVASE	Well, think about it. Do you remember, after the play finished last year, we couldn't find the prompt-book? It's my guess Richard took it and he's now seeing his chance to make a bit of money by selling it to Dickon.
GEOFFREY	We don't know that anybody took the prompt-book – it was probably thrown out with the rubbish. But what if he were selling it to Dickon? Dozens of city people came out to see our cycle last year – any of them could have gone home and written out most of the script from memory. There's no way of keeping it secret.
GERVASE	But the prompt-book has all our moves written on it, all the notes we made in rehearsals, everything. *(He is called by one of the players.)* I'm just saying watch him, Geoffrey.

80

(GERVASE returns to the crowd; HARRY brings in food and drink. Everybody turns hopefully to GEOFFREY, who smiles reluctantly.)

90

GEOFFREY	All right, take a five-minute break.

(They cheer.)

But then we're running scene one again – this time with no scripts!

(As the actors concerned protest, and everyone else mocks them, the lights dim.)

---

prompt-book *An extremely important and valuable copy of the complete script, on which notes were made about actors' movements, props needed and any other decisions made during rehearsals.*

SCENE 3

*Day two of rehearsals. As the lights come up, we sense a real atmosphere of
concentration. The actors are 'on-stage', having apparently just run through a scene.*

GEOFFREY	That was good, but we've got to get through the feet-washing faster.	1

SYMKIN   Does he actually have to wash everybody's feet? Couldn't
he do a few and then have the conversation with Peter?

GEOFFREY   Possibly. We'll try it that way and see if it works. Katherine,
can I just check a few things about the props . . .

*(As he goes over to KATHERINE, general conversations break out
as people relax after a difficult hour. ROBIN takes the
opportunity to check out the story with MARION.)*

ROBIN   Right, there are two things I don't understand.   10

MARION   Go on.

ROBIN   This is the Last Supper, right? Jesus has got all the disciples
together for the Feast of the Passover. *(She nods.)* Well,
what's the feet-washing about?

MARION   It's difficult to say, but he seems to be telling them that, just
as he washed their feet, they must wash each others – not
be too proud about it, I suppose. It's something to do with
humility and love.

ROBIN   I think I see. The other thing is – does he actually know
that Judas is going to betray him?   20

MARION   Oh yes.

---

 humility *The quality of being humble and modest; not thinking that you
are better than other people.*

ROBIN	That must be very hard.
MARION	It is. Very hard.
GEOFFREY	*(Calling out.)* Right! Let's try it again, this time with the furniture and the rest of the props. Scene two: the Last Supper!

(JANKIN and HODGE bring on the trestle table and then join the others behind it in a representation of the Last Supper – something like the picture captured a few centuries later by Leonardo da Vinci. GEOFFREY, as JESUS, stands centre, behind the table. On each side of him are the rest of the cast, representing the 12 disciples.)

30

Leonardo da Vinci *The Italian artist, who painted a famous picture of the Last Supper in 1495.*

JESUS	The Feast of Passover is come.
	Peace to this house and all that's here.
	Bring me a bowl of water clean,
	Andrew, my disciple dear.

(ANDREW brings water and places it on the floor in front of the table, where JESUS has taken up his position.)

	Now will I wash your feet, each one,
	And Andrew first, God's will be done.

40

(They all walk round and JESUS washes their feet.)

You see that I have work in hand . . .

PETER	*(Refusing to have his feet washed.)*
	. . . But why I cannot understand.
	Ah, gracious master, by your leave,
	This service makes me sorely grieve.
JESUS	*(Sternly.)* Peter, take this humility,
	Or never share heaven's bliss with me.
PETER	*(Appalled by JESUS's words.)*
	Forget my words, lord, pardon me!
	For out of that bliss I'll never be!
	Wash on, my master, scrub away!
	Feet, hands and everything, I pray!

50

(The rest of the actors laugh at GERVASE's enthusiastic delivery.)

GERVASE	What's the matter? Did I say something funny?
GEOFFREY	*(Still laughing.)* It was perfect, Gervase. A bit more enthusiastic than before, that's all. But keep it just like that! Let's go straight on with the scene, shall we.

Passover *The spring festival which commemorated the flight of the Israelites from Egypt and the passing over by the Angel of Death of the Jews' houses, so that only the Egyptian first-born sons were killed.*

makes me sorely grieve *Causes me to be extremely unhappy.*

(They quickly get back into character. Andrew passes Jesus the bread from the table and he breaks it up offering some to each of the disciples.)   60

JESUS   Now have we shared this holy feast . . .
But one that hath broken bread with me
Will prove to be my enemy.

(There is a moment of silent shock from the disciples, but JESUS goes on, dipping a piece of bread into a bowl of wine.)

The traitor is in this company . . .
Judas, receive this bread from me.

(RICHARD stretches out his hand to accept the bread, but it drops to the ground. There is a tense silence as GEOFFREY and RICHARD look at each other.)   70

RICHARD   It slipped.

GEOFFREY   Don't worry. I was going to stop there anyway . . . *(Then, to the whole cast.)* We're all very tired and I don't think we can get much further with this tonight. Thank you everybody.

(As they all leave, collecting up the props as they go, GEOFFREY finds himself next to RICHARD.)

You worked hard tonight. Good.

RICHARD   I'm trying.

   80

GEOFFREY   I know. *(As RICHARD leaves.)* Look over your lines for tomorrow: it's that tricky scene in the Garden of Gethsemane.

(RICHARD nods and leaves as the lights come down on GEOFFREY, scribbling notes on his script.)

the Garden of Gethsemane *The garden on the Mount of Olives, east of Jerusalem, where Jesus was to be arrested on Judas's information.*

SCENE 4

Day three of rehearsals. The actors are at the end of a break, eating, drinking and talking. GEOFFREY calls them to order.

GEOFFREY	I'd like to move straight on now to the garden scene and take it through to the end without stopping, if we can.	1

(There is a great deal of page-turning as they find their places, and we hear exchanges such as: 'Is that from Scene 11?' '12, I think.' 'Right.')

(ROBIN sidles up to MARION, frantically leafing through his script and clearly panicking slightly.)

ROBIN   I haven't looked at this bit yet.

MARION   It's quite straightforward. It's the part where Jesus and the disciples are in a garden outside the town and he knows   10
that this will be the night Judas betrays him to the Romans and the priests. Don't tell me you don't know the story!

ROBIN   I do know it. Judas comes in and identifies Jesus to the guards by kissing him.

MARION   That's right.

(She studies ROBIN as, for the first time, the impact of the story really dawns on him.)

ROBIN   How awful!

GEOFFREY   *(Announcing.)* Scene 12: The Garden of Gethsemane.

*(GEOFFREY takes his place as JESUS, others playing the disciples   20
lie down some way off; RICHARD as JUDAS, HUBERT as CAYAPHAS and a few others playing soldiers, wait to one side.)*

(JESUS kneels and prays.)

JESUS   I am so afraid, Father, for I know what is planned
And the hour of my torment is almost at hand.

My disciples are daunted and fearful of heart;
I must comfort them, Father, and then we must part.

(He moves to the disciples and wakes them.)

Now Peter and Andrew, Philip and John,
You must be of good cheer, let your worries be gone.

30

(JESUS looks up at JUDAS, who has arrived with CAYAPHAS and the soldiers.)

For found is the friend we have come here to meet;
Our company's gathered. All is complete.

JUDAS   And this is my master, the man that I seek.
May I greet you, my lord, with a kiss on your cheek?

JESUS   Most heartily, Judas. *(JUDAS kisses him.)*
Now the debt will be paid;
For with this one kiss mankind's Son is betrayed.

(GEOFFREY and RICHARD remain together for a second and the other actors seem to freeze.)

40

RICHARD   I'm sorry, Geoffrey.

GEOFFREY   Don't be. It's only a play.

(Still in the same position, looking straight at RICHARD, GEOFFREY announces:)

Cut straight to Scene 13: the remorse of Judas.

(All the actors except RICHARD leave the stage. There is absolute silence for his speech.)

the hour of my torment *Jesus knows that he will soon be arrested, tried and crucified (see the Introduction, page 29).*

daunted *They had lost their courage.*

mankind's Son *Jesus is sometimes known as the Son of Man.*

JUDAS   I am suddenly stricken with conscience and guilt.
           The kindness he showed me was candid and felt.   50

           (Enter ANNAS, CAYAPHAS and PILATE.)

           The master I sold you was loving to me:
           You can take back your silver. Let him walk free!

ANNAS   We've no interest, Judas, in your change of heart . . .

CAYAPHAS   . . . The bargain you bought was your plan from the start.

PILATE   We had an agreement and both of us win:
           I have my 'Son of Man'. You have your sin.

           *(As he utters his final words, and leaves with ANNAS and
           CAYAPHAS, PILATE throws the bag of silver at JUDAS.)*

           (Alone on stage, JUDAS sinks to his knees and allows the coins   60
           to drop from the bag on to the floor.)

JUDAS   My treacherous turn torments me with fire;
           Now Judas forever is famed as a liar,
           And ages to come will curse bitterly when
           They spit the name Judas, betrayer of men.
           This direst of deeds cannot undo nor mend,
           I have no one to turn to, no brother nor friend;
           My body I'll raise *(He stands and takes a noose from his
           jacket.)* but my soul must descend,
           As mankind's beginning marks Judas's end.   70

           *(There is a long silence, in which RICHARD stands, staring out
           into the distance, the noose dangling from his hand, and one by
           one the players leave the stage, clearly impressed by his
           performance, picking up their bits and pieces as they go.)*

  candid *Honest and straightforward in his behaviour; not hiding anything,
or trying to deceive.*

	(Left alone, RICHARD turns and approaches the chest, takes out his key, opens the lid and replaces the bag which had been nestling in his jacket throughout the rehearsal. Leaving the lid open, he slumps back against the chest, as though exhausted, when GEOFFREY re-enters.)	
GEOFFREY	Tired? I'm not surprised. Rehearsals take it out of you. Come and join us . . . we're going for a drink. *(Noticing the open chest.)* Oh . . . sorting out the savings?	80
RICHARD	No, no . . . I found this. *(Reaching into the chest.)* I suppose I must have put it there by mistake last year . . . *(He brings out a wad of papers loosely bound into a book.)* It's the prompt-book . . . The one you thought was lost?	
GEOFFREY	*(Kneeling down and taking the book from him, he speaks very gently.)* Ah, yes. But I didn't think it was completely lost, Richard.	
RICHARD	No. I'm glad.	90
GEOFFREY	*(Standing briskly.)* Come on, I'm thirsty. *(He starts to walk off, but turns, as RICHARD stands up.)* Oh. That Judas part . . .	
RICHARD	*(Concerned.)* Yes? You said you wanted to make changes?	
GEOFFREY	I said I wanted to see how it worked . . . And I think it works pretty well as it is.	
	(He leaves. RICHARD locks the chest, picks it up, tucks it safely under his arm and walks out.)	

ACTING Rehearse and then perform the scene in which Geoffrey asks Richard to repeat his 'trust me . . .' line (from 'Stop a moment . . .' to 'Yes' (pages 40 – 41). First discuss why Geoffrey does this and think what each character might be thinking during the scene.

FREEZE-FRAME In groups of six, playing Geoffrey, Richard, Marion, Alyson, Gervase and one other actor, freeze-frame the moment in Scene 3 when Richard drops the bread (page 46). First think carefully about your own character's reactions to that incident.

WRITING: DISCUSSION Write Geoffrey's diary for the second day of rehearsals. What is he feeling about the play and about Richard?

As a class, discuss the possible meanings of 'I'm sorry, Geoffrey.' (page 48). Why is that line important for the story of Geoffrey and Richard?

HOT-SEATING Look back through all the things that Marion and Robin say about Marion's son, Geoffrey.

In groups of four, hot-seat Marion, asking her how she feels about him and the way he deals with people.

Or: Look back at Richard's behaviour in the play and hot-seat him, asking him why he had a change of heart and decided to return both the money and the prompt-book.

LANGUAGE STUDY The script of the mystery play that the actors are reading from is written in the same style as the original mystery plays: some of the lines rhyme and there is also a good deal of alliteration.

Look back at the extracts from the script and pick out the examples of alliteration. Then write a scene of your own in the same style, using some alliteration and some rhyme. (It could be a scene for a completely different story, or one that would fit this episode, such as Judas giving us his reasons for deciding to betray Jesus.)

DISCUSSION In pairs, discuss what evidence there is to back up each of the following statements:
- Geoffrey knows all along exactly what Richard has been up to.
- Marion knows as well, and realises how much her son must be hurt by Richard's actions.
- Geoffrey deliberately behaves during rehearsals in such a way as to make Richard aware of what he has done.
- The play shows that it is better for Richard to put the money back himself and return the prompt-book, rather than be exposed as a thief by the others.
- *Mystery Play* is about the power of drama to make people think about themselves and their actions.

DISCUSSION AND NOTE-MAKING The story of Geoffrey and Richard has many parallels with, or echoes of, the Bible story of Jesus and Judas that they are rehearsing.

Discuss what the parallels are, using this grid as a framework. One example has been filled in to start you off:

The GEOFFREY & RICHARD STORY	page	The JESUS & JUDAS STORY
Geoffrey's mother is called Marion	oo	
Richard is the company treasurer	oo	
Geoffrey is the guild master who writes the script	oo	
Gervase is always in a bad temper	oo	He plays Peter, the hot-tempered disciple.
Richard appears to be planning to betray Geoffrey by selling the prompt-book to a rival company.	oo	
Richard says 'I'm sorry, Geoffrey.'	oo	
Richard puts the money back.	oo	

Are there any other echoes or parallels with the Bible story?
- What about the cock crowing? Or the full title of the play?
- Or the fact that Geoffrey carries the heavy responsibility of always playing Jesus?
- What are the essential differences between the Bible story and the story of Geoffrey and Richard? (Think especially about the ways in which they end.)

Dramascripts
Sir Gawain and the Green Knight

A version of the medieval English epic poem

David Calcutt

INTRODUCTION

THE POEM

The epic poem *Sir Gawain and the Green Knight* exists as a single manuscript, which is now kept in the British Museum. It was written in the late 14th Century by an unknown poet who lived in the north west Midlands, and wrote in the dialect of that region.

But we know very little else about him, except that he was educated, and knew English, French and Latin. He most likely lived in one of the great castles of Staffordshire or Derbyshire, perhaps as secretary or chaplain. Besides *Sir Gawain* he wrote three other poems, *Purity, Patience* and *Pearl,* in which he mourns the death of his infant daughter.

THE MYTH OF ARTHUR

Sir Gawain and the Green Knight draws upon a tradition of stories and legends about King Arthur that was already some 600 years old when the poem was written. If there was a real Arthur, he was most likely a Roman-British war-leader living in the early 5th Century who managed, for a while, to check the invasion of Saxon tribes, and bring a period of peace to the country.

From this rose the myth of a Golden Age ruled over by a magical king and his wonder-working knights, surviving in oral-form among the Celtic peoples of Wales, Ireland, Cornwall and Brittany. It wasn't until the year 1136 that a full account of Arthur's life was written down, by Geoffrey of Monmouth in his book *Historia Regum Britanniae (The History of the Kings of Britain)*.

Shortly after that, the French writer Chrétien de Troyes began to write a series of Arthurian stories, and other works quickly followed. It was the work of Chrétien de Troyes, and those that followed him, that first gave Arthur and his warriors the form of a medieval king and his knights, fighting to uphold the medieval values of honour and chivalry.

But it was the English knight, Sir Thomas Malory, living some 200 years later, who set down all the important Arthurian stories in a single work – *Morte D'Arthur (The Death of Arthur)*. This was completed in 1469–70, and printed by William Caxton in 1485. It is this single work that has given us the story as we know it today, and which continues to flourish in poems, novels, music and films.

CHIVALRY AND HONOUR

The code of chivalry developed among the aristocratic French and English knights of the 12th Century, from a simple code of military behaviour to a complex and refined system of behaviour that governed every aspect of life both on and off the battlefield.

The main features of this code were devotion to women, and the protection of the weak and defenceless. It was the idealised love for a noble, and unattainable woman, that inspired a knight to acts of honour and chivalry, to seek out and defend the weak against tyranny, and risk all hazards and dangers, even death, in her name. As the stories of Arthur and his knights developed, they came to stand for the ideal of this code, with Sir Gawain as its most perfect example. The code, and its testing, lie at the heart of the poem *Sir Gawain and the Green Knight.*

SETTING AND BACKGROUND

Sir Gawain and the Green Knight is performed by a group of travelling players, living in England at the end of the 14th Century, which is also the period when the actual poem was written. The final decades of that century were particularly unstable, seeing the Peasants Revolt of 1381, an outbreak of plague, and the deposing and murder of the king, Richard II.

But it was also a period that saw the first flowering of English literature, with the writings of the *Sir Gawain* poet, Geoffrey Chaucer, William Langland and others. It was also the period that saw the creation of the great mystery plays cycles – the first true English drama, which reached its culmination in the Elizabethan theatre of Marlowe and Shakespeare, a century later. See the *Mystery Play* also in this *Dramascript.*

THIS PLAY

In setting *Sir Gawain and the Green Knight* as a play performed by a group of medieval travelling players, the playwright has tried to remain true both to the spirit of the original poem, and to the tradition of such medieval plays, while at the same time being aware that it's being written for a 20th Century audience.

In the language, the poetry and narrative are emphasised, while the drama and theatre arise from the setting itself: the creation of the mythical and magical world of the story from a few simple but effective props and pieces of costume, in an empty space, that can become any place and time.

THE CHARACTERS

Six players who take the following parts:

ARTHUR

GUINEVERE

SIR GAWAIN

MORGANA/NINEVE

GREEN KNIGHT

BERTILAK

THE PLAY

An empty stage. A group of travelling PLAYERS enter, hauling a large, wooden cart. Piled on the cart are a jumble of costumes, props, and masks. The PLAYERS are raggedly dressed, though their clothes show some of the faded glory and gaudiness of their profession. Wearily, they bring the cart to a halt, and speak to the audience.

1st PLAYER	Hard times, they were, with the war bringing ruin to the land. Brother against brother, father against son. Towns burning, black smoke in the air, the whole country laid waste. Only the crows and the wolves grew fat.	1
2nd PLAYER	Fearful times, when hot summer brought the plague. Black crosses on the doors, the windows shuttered. From inside, the sounds of weeping or silence. God's face was hidden and death rode in the air.	
3rd PLAYER	Mean times, for poor players travelling the road. All houses were closed to us, no kind word or welcome. We begged them for crusts, and they served us with curses. Sharp looks and hard stones drove us onward.	10
4th PLAYER	And autumn brought the bad weather, howling wind and driving rain. And winter brought the freezing cold, and a deep frost that almost cracked our hearts. Like homeless birds we wandered. We sought for shelter and found none.	
5th PLAYER	Strangers we were in an unknown country, a desolate place, far from our own land. No dwelling we found, no place of human habitation. In the days that followed, three of us died. The ground was too hard for graves. We left them by the roadside.	20
6th PLAYER	At last we came to the dried-up bed of a river, and a sheer hill rising, and the black mouth of a cave. Wearily we	

climbed that bleak crag, with the last of our strength we stumbled inside. Our long road ended here, in the hill's dark. We lit a small fire for warmth. Exhausted, we slept.

(As they speak, now, the PLAYERS dress themselves in costumes from the cart, and take on the roles of the characters they will play. It is as if the dream they are describing is gradually coming to life in them.) 30

1st PLAYER And as we slept, we dreamed.

2nd PLAYER And it was the same dream.

3rd PLAYER All of us dreaming that same dream.

4th PLAYER A dream of a fair country, green, and rolling . . .

5th PLAYER Where a tree blossomed on a sunlit hilltop . . .

6th PLAYER Bearing leaves of silver, apples of gold . . .

1st PLAYER That shone together like the moon and the sun.

2nd PLAYER And we knew that our dream was a dream of Britain . . .

3rd PLAYER Arthur's kingdom, country of wonders . . .

4th PLAYER Where marvels were many . . . 40

5th PLAYER And the earth sang them . . .

6th PLAYER And the dream that we had was a tale of those times.

(The PLAYERS now begin to perform the play of their dream. To create the play and its characters, and locations, they use the cart and the costumes and props from the cart.)

ARTHUR And one time Arthur was at Camelot . . .

GUINEVERE With Guinevere his queen, where they kept court . . .

Arthur's kingdom *The kingdom of Britain under the reign of King Arthur, which is seen as a mythical Golden Age, in sharp contrast to the age in which the players live.*

SIR GAWAIN	With the noblest lords and ladies gathered . . .
ARTHUR	For celebration of the New Year feast.
GUINEVERE	Torches blazed in the hall.
SIR GAWAIN	Firelight flickered.
ARTHUR	Bright tapestries hung from the shining walls.
GUINEVERE	All manner of fare adorned the tables . . .
SIR GAWAIN	And there was music and merriment . . .
ARTHUR	Laughter and song . . .
GUINEVERE	Sounds of mirth and well-being, glorious to hear.
SIR GAWAIN	For they were young, and in the spring of youth . . .
ARTHUR	No sorrow known to them, no grief nor dole . . .
GUINEVERE	A noble company, favoured on earth . . .
SIR GAWAIN	No shadow upon them, no dark in the soul.
GUINEVERE	Then Arthur spoke. Arthur, who had pulled the sword from the stone; Arthur, law-giver, the heaven-chosen king. He rose from his seat and stood in the hall, and he spoke.

50

60

(ARTHUR speaks as if to the assembled court.)

ARTHUR	I've heard how, in olden times gone by,
	It was the custom, at this time of year,
	For the king to let no morsel pass his lips
	Till he had heard some tale of wonderment,
	Or seen some marvel, that would astonish
	And delight. This I make my custom now,
	And vow to neither eat or drink,
	Till I have witnessed such a wonder here.

70

> **Camelot** *Arthur's capital. If there was a real Arthur, and a real Camelot, it might have been situated at Cadbury Hillfort in Somerset.*
>
> **dole** *Sadness.*

(The ACTORS speak to the audience.)

MORGANA And out in the world, beyond the blazing fires and the glittering windows, out beyond the shining towers of Camelot, in the wild and winter wastes of the untamed world, something heard him, and answered his prayer.

GUINEVERE And our voices fell silent as we heard it approaching . . .

SIR GAWAIN Like a cold wind driving down out of the North . . .

ARTHUR The kind that brings storms and the weltering snow . . .   80

GUINEVERE Only this time bringing something worse . . .

SIR GAWAIN As it raged round the hall like a pack of dogs howling . . .

ARTHUR And beat on the doors like a beast from the mountain . . .

GUINEVERE And the doors splintered and burst wide open . . .

SIR GAWAIN And a terrible figure strode into the hall!

MORGANA Hair crowned with holly, yew-sprig and ivy,
Cloak made of rat's-tails, fox-pelt, and crow-feather,
Wolf-fang,
Boar-tusk,
Stag-hoof and axe-head,   90
Lord of the Wild Things, King of the Wood!

(The GREEN KNIGHT is brought on by BERTILAK and NINEVE.)

BERTILAK A marvel was this man,
A wonder to be seen.

Morgana *Morgana is better known as* **Morgan Le Faye.** *She was Arthur's half-sister, and his deadly enemy. In some versions of the story, she seduces Arthur and it is their child, Mordred, who brings about the death of Arthur and the end of the* Golden Age.

Lord of the Wild Things . . . *The Green Knight is probably a memory of a pre-Christian, pagan god of nature.*

NINEVE	His body broad and brawn And over-all bright green.
	(The GREEN KNIGHT stands central.)
ARTHUR	And we stared at him in awe.
GUINEVERE	In amazement we gazed on this green figure . . . 100
SIR GAWAIN	This creature that had suddenly come among us . . .
ARTHUR	As if stepping out of our worst nightmare
GUINEVERE	Or from the very rim of the world's beginning,
SIR GAWAIN	One of earth's first creatures, risen from its resting-place.
ARTHUR	And he gazed at each of us in turn . . .
GUINEVERE	Fixed us each with his eyes, as if to hold us here . . .
ARTHUR	And, holding us fixed here, he spoke.
	(The GREEN KNIGHT makes his challenge.)
GREEN KNIGHT	Who's leader here? Which is your king? I would speak with him. 110
ARTHUR	I am. Arthur's my name. This is my court. What do you want here?
GREEN KNIGHT	I've come to offer you a game.
ARTHUR	A game?
GREEN KNIGHT	A Midwinter Game. And if there's any here bold enough and fearless enough to play this game with me, let him step forward now.

The Green Knight is brought on . . . *To emphasise the otherworldly nature of the Green Knight, he can be portrayed as a larger-than-life size figure or puppet, operated by the two actors playing Bertilak and Nineve. The Green Knight's lines may be spoken by one, or both of these actors.*

NINEVE *The pronunciation is* Nin-e-ve *with the – e – short.*

ARTHUR	Before any of us agrees, perhaps you should tell us first the rules of this Midwinter Game.
GREEN KNIGHT	They're simple enough. An exchange of blows, that's all 120 I ask. There's an axe at my belt. It's good and sharp. Let you, or one of your knights, take it in his hands. Let him strike a single blow at me. I'll stand and take it. I won't flinch. And, if I should survive that blow, then I claim the right to deal the same to him. Those are the rules. What could be simpler? So, who'll play this game with me? Hurry. Give me an answer. I'm impatient to begin.
SIR GAWAIN	But no one spoke.
GUINEVERE	Not a whisper or word.
SIR GAWAIN	No one moved. 130
GUINEVERE	We just sat and stared
SIR GAWAIN	As if this creature had cast a spell . . .
GUINEVERE	Freezing out tongues and our limbs as well . . .
SIR GAWAIN	And he stood there among us in the silent room . . .
GUINEVERE	And drew back his head, and his great voice boomed.
GREEN KNIGHT	No one? Not one of you? Is this the famed bravery of Arthur's knights? Perhaps I've come to the wrong place. Or perhaps the stories they tell about you are lies. It doesn't matter. I'll leave you to your eating and drinking, and find 140 my entertainment somewhere else.
ARTHUR	Wait! You'll have your . . . entertainment. We're not lacking in courage here. Give me the axe. I'll accept your challenge.
GUINEVERE	No! You must not do this. There's too much risk.
ARTHUR	Since when have I shirked danger because of that?
GUINEVERE	You're the king.
ARTHUR	And as the king I take up this challenge.

GUINEVERE	And as the king you cannot. Remember who you are. Remember what you are. A king's the heart of the kingdom, its spirit, its soul. No king on the throne, no life in the land. Nominate a champion, someone to stand in your place. Let another strike the blow. This game's not for you.
GREEN KNIGHT	Whether it's you, or another makes no odds to me. A man to strike this blow is all I need. For the last time of asking, is my challenge accepted. Who'll come forward and take up this axe?
SIR GAWAIN	I will. Arthur's nephew, his sister's son. I'll stand for my king, I'm eager for fame, Let me take up the axe, I'll play this game.

(*ARTHUR and GAWAIN narrate as GAWAIN and the GREEN KNIGHT exchange words and enact what is described.*)

ARTHUR	And Gawain steps forward.
SIR GAWAIN	One blow you said?
GUINEVERE	He takes up the axe.
GREEN KNIGHT	A single blow only.
ARTHUR	He feels its edge.
SIR GAWAIN	You'll stand and receive it?
GUINEVERE	It's sharp and keen.
GREEN KNIGHT	As you will in return.

150

160

170

No king on the throne, no life in the land *A widespread ancient belief, to be found in all cultures, is that the well-being of the earth resides in the life of a people's leader or king. As long as the king is well, the land is well. If the king sickens or dies, so does the land. This idea is crucially important to people whose very existence depends on the fruitfulness of the earth.*

SIR GAWAIN	As I will in my turn, upon my honour.
GREEN KNIGHT	Good. Here's my neck. Lift the axe and strike.
ARTHUR	Gawain lifts the axe, feels its weight poised . . .
GUINEVERE	A moment suspended between rising and falling . . .
ARTHUR	Then he brings it down, its bright blade flashing . . .
GUINEVERE	And strikes off the head with a single blow!

(MORGANA narrates.)

MORGANA	He struck off the head, he saw it fall,
	And a cry of wonder rose through the hall,
	As the figure stooped down, grasped its head by the hair
	And lifted it high into the air
	And with a voice as harsh as a raven's croak
	The bloody head opened its mouth and spoke.

GREEN KNIGHT	I've survived your blow. Now you must stand and let me strike at you. But not now. I give you a year's grace. My home's in the North. Men know me there, and my dwelling-place. Twelvemonth hence, on New Year's morning, seek me at the place of the Green Chapel. And there receive such a blow as you've given here. Keep this bargain, knight, if you value your honour. A year from now I'll be waiting, and my axe will be sharp.

(BERTILAK and NINEVE remove the GREEN KNIGHT as others narrate.)

180

190

200

ARTHUR	Then he was gone.	
GUINEVERE	To what land no one knew.	
ARTHUR	All were silent in the hall.	
GUINEVERE	There was nothing to be said.	
ARTHUR	Night was falling.	
GUINEVERE	The feast was over.	
ARTHUR	We put out the torches.	210
GUINEVERE	We went to our beds.	

SIR GAWAIN   And Gawain stood alone in the gathering dark. Outside in the courtyard, in the midwinter's night. Above him, a black sky filled with glittering stars, the cold fires of heaven, a frost-white moon. He heard an owl shriek, he heard a fox bark, he heard the wind weeping over the grasses. And he felt the ice crack in his heart, and the touch of the cold like a blade at his throat.

(To show the passing of time, all the ACTORS now sing or speak the following.)   220

ALL   Winter lies bound
Like a man in his chains
And longs for the spring
And the sweet falling rain.

Warm sun and showers
Bring blossom to bloom
And the dead that were buried
Break free from their tomb.

And walk the bright earth
Dressed in robes of pure light   230
And sing with the skylarks
A song of delight.

A fair youth shakes his hair
Of bright burning gold

And summer's rich bounty
Swiftly unfolds.

The rich, rolling hills,
The swift, shining streams
All seen as if
In a wondrous dream.

240

But the dream quickly fades
And passes away
And all that has grown
Soon begins to decay.

The year gives up its sweetness
Like ripe autumn fruit
That drops from its tree
With a worm in its heart.

The sky's heavy with cloud
The wind's sharp and chill
And winter rides forth
With his hounds to the kill.

250

As the year turns its wheel
On the hard, stony track
And rolls ever forward
And never looks back.

So we go to our graves
And all earth does mourn
And lie in the ground
And wait to be born.

260

(GAWAIN steps forward and narrates.)

SIR GAWAIN   Towards the year's end, my thoughts turned to the bargain
I'd made, and the journey I must undertake. And so, on
All-Hallows' Day, I put on my armour and weapons, and
saddled my horse, and took my leave of Arthur and
Guinevere.

(He turns to ARTHUR and GUINEVERE.)

ARTHUR	God speed you on your quest, Gawain, and with His blessing speed you safely back here to us.

GUINEVERE	My blessing also go with you, dear Gawain. And take this kiss. *(She kisses him.)* May it keep us in your thoughts, and afford some comfort in your trials to come.	270

(GAWAIN narrates.)

SIR GAWAIN	Then I mounted my horse and spurred him on , and his hooves struck sparks from the stone of the courtyard, as we passed through the gates of Camelot, and they closed behind me, and we set forth upon the open road.

(Between them, MORGANA, GAWAIN, BERTILAK and NINEVE narrate GAWAIN's journey.)

MORGANA	Now rides this knight through the realm . . .	280

BERTILAK	Leaves behind him comrades, kingdom . . .

 All-Hallows' Day *November 1st, the day after* All-Hallows' Eve, *or* Hallowe'en. *It is also known as* All Saints' Day.

NINEVE	Travels northward to the wild lands . . .
BERTILAK	Makes his way through fell and fastness . . .
MORGANA	Leaves his own world, leaves the known world . . .
BERTILAK	Lost and lone in countries strange.
SIR GAWAIN	It was hard going through rough country, places I, or no man, had ever seen before. Tall crags towered high above me, water dropped in torrents from clifftops, plunged, boiling and foaming into deep pools. Far from home, I was, alone and without companion or friend, a stranger to these wasted lands. But my faith spurred me on, gave me heart and hope. I put my trust in my courage and my strength of arms.

290

MORGANA	See the earth call forth her creatures . . .
BERTILAK	See them crawl from marsh and cave-mouth . . .
NINEVE	Filled with hatred, filled with hunger . . .
BERTILAK	Sliding from the roots of mountains . . .
MORGANA	Howling in the heart of forests . . .
BERTILAK	Night's own creatures, hell's sweet children.
SIR GAWAIN	I fought with dragons and wolves, bulls and wild bears. Sometimes with trolls that came down from the mountains, and monsters that have no name in any language. All the terrible creatures of that country pursued me. Many times I was close to death. I lost my sword and my spear, my shield

300

fell *Moorland.*

trolls *A creature from Norse myth, born from rock. If the sun's rays touched it, it returned to stone.*

for heaven made my arm strong *Gawain, as a Christian knight, is being pitted against creatures from the pagan world. At the heart of the story and the play, is a struggle between the Christian and pagan worlds.*

was broken, but my heart never failed, for heaven made my arm strong, and I had God's strength to protect me.

BERTILAK   Hear the wind-blast in the treetops . . .

NINEVE   Hear the howl of winter weather . . .

BERTILAK   Lost inside the storm he wanders . . .

MORGANA   Driven deep within the tempest . . .   310

BERTILAK   Where the lightning cracks its fire . . .

NINEVE   And the thunder drums his doom.

SIR GAWAIN   On the first day of the storm came the sleet and the freezing rain. Arrows of ice shattered my armour, and I cast it aside. I looked for somewhere to shelter but there was none. The second day brought raging winds and a sky black as night. I saw no sun, and the storm drove me onwards. On the third day there was no respite. Frozen to the bone I tried to push forward, but my horse stumbled and fell and died under me. I knew I could go no further. So I cut open   320
its belly and crawled inside, and lay there for shelter against the bad weather.

BERTILAK   Here's a man in rags and tatters . . .

NINEVE   Here's a creature shaved and shorn . . .

BERTILAK   Robbed of all that he possesses . . .

MORGANA   Rendered to the elemental . . .

BERTILAK   Man as was and always shall be . . .

NINEVE   Thing of hair and blood and bone.

SIR GAWAIN   When I woke the storm had passed. There was a clear sky, bright and cold. I was on a bare hillside. Frozen earth, grass   330
stiff with frost. Nearby, in a hollow, a circle of stones, fallen, broken, centuries old. I looked around at the bleak landscape. No bird flew. No creature crawled. Nothing moved. There was no sound. Beyond this, there was

nothing. I sat still. I didn't move. I had come to the end of the world, and there was nowhere else to go.

MORGANA/
BERTILAK/
NINEVE

And all that remains
Are his pride and his name
That burn like a flame
In the cave of his brain 340
Where he sits without fear
Like a wolf in its lair
And howls out his prayer
To the cold, empty air.

SIR GAWAIN Lady Mary, Mother of God, Most Holy and Gracious Queen of Heaven. Hear me, I beseech you. Send me succour and aid, let me find shelter, that I may not perish here in this wilderness. Not out of faint heart nor fear of death do I beg this favour, but that I may not fail to fulfil my quest, which I have undertaken for thy glory and honour, for all that I 350 do is done in praise of thy name.

BERTILAK And this is how heaven answers his prayer . . .

MORGANA With a jag of black lightning that cracks from the sky . . .

BERTILAK And pierces him through and splits him wide . . .

MORGANA From the crown of his head to the sole of his foot . . .

BERTILAK And the world shudders and buckles and turns inside out . . .

NINEVE And swallows him up in its smoking hole . . .

BERTILAK And the grasses tremble . . .

MORGANA And the wind sighs . . .

BERTILAK And a shadow passes, and the hillside's empty. 360

(*ARTHUR and GUINEVERE now narrate.*)

ARTHUR Asleep on the hilltop, Gawain had a dream.

GUINEVERE In this dream he saw the stones in the hollow begin to move.

ARTHUR	As if moved by some invisible power, they rose from the earth and began to re-arrange themselves.
GUINEVERE	Or as if the stones themselves were only the outward, physical form of something hidden, something much more wonderful and marvellous, emerging and revealed now, its inward form displayed.
ARTHUR	A castle. A castle of stone now stood there on the hilltop, its walls and towers rising high above him, its carved, wooden gates open and leading to the courtyard beyond.
GUINEVERE	And in his dream, there was an old woman standing beside the gates, and she beckoned to him and bowed when he approached, and then she spoke.

(MORGANA approaches GAWAIN.)

MORGANA	This way, sir knight. I'll lead you to my master's and mistress's home. It lies through these gates. They'll give you welcome and treat you well. Come, sir. This way. Here you'll find all that you've come to seek.
ARTHUR	And then in his dream he followed the old woman through the gates, and into the courtyard where all was silent and empty . . .
GUINEVERE	As if the whole castle was deserted, but it wasn't, for she led him up through a doorway where many stone creatures were carved . . .
ARTHUR	And into a great hall hung with tapestries, where a fire burned and torches flickered . . .
GUINEVERE	And coming forward to greet him, hands extended in friendship, were the Lord and the Lady of the castle.

(BERTILAK and NINEVE approach GAWAIN.)

BERTILAK	You're welcome here, sir. Welcome! My name's Bertilak. This castle's my home.
NINEVE	And I'm Nineve, my Lord's wife, and Lady of this house.

370

380

390

BERTILAK As for your own name, and where you're from, and what purpose has brought you to our bleak, northern country . . . 400

NINEVE There's no need yet to tell us that. There'll be time enough for questions and their answers.

BERTILAK First you must eat, and drink, and take your rest. For you're our guest and welcome to treat everything here as you please. 410

NINEVE What comforts we have shall be given gladly. All is yours to have and use as you wish.

ARTHUR Then a chair was brought, and food and drink . . .

GUINEVERE And he sat before the fire, a guest of honour . . .

ARTHUR And the Lady's servant placed a cloak upon his shoulders . . .

GUINEVERE A mantle of silk, embroidered with ermine . . .

ARTHUR And he was handsomely served, and treated with courtesy . . . 42

GUINEVERE Though it was strange that in all that castle there was no other servant but that one old woman . . .

NINEVE Bertilak's wife is given no name in the poem. The name I've given her is one of the names of the Lady of the Lake in the Arthurian story, Morte d'Arthur by Sir Thomas Malory. (See Introduction, page 54.)

ARTHUR   And she was a wrinkled, ancient creature, bent almost double, and eyes pale as the moon . . .

GUINEVERE   But this was a dream, where strangeness is commonplace . . .

ARTHUR   And the food was good and the wine was warming . . .

GUINEVERE   And his head was light and his hosts were charming . . .

ARTHUR   And they seemed so enamoured of their new-arrived guest . . .   430

GUINEVERE   And he told them his name, his purpose and his quest.

(BERTILAK and NINEVE speak to GAWAIN.)

BERTILAK   Gawain! You are indeed welcome! We've heard of you, of course. Your name and fame, your honour and renown, are widely known.

NINEVE   That a knight of Arthur's court, and by all reports, the noblest and best of that breed, should grace us with his presence, is an honour indeed.

BERTILAK   As for your quest, you're in the right place. The Green Chapel lies not far from here. Two miles, no more.   440

NINEVE   But you have three days before your appointed time. Why don't you pass them here with us? Stay, and take your ease. And fortify yourself against the trial to come.

BERTILAK   You'll be doing us a favour. For we shall have the chance to witness, at first hand, how men of breeding bear themselves, and to savour all the delights of courtly behaviour.

honour and renown *It's not for his bravery or prowess as a warrior that Gawain is chiefly known, but for his* honour. *The importance to a knight of honour, and the code of chivalry, play a great part in the poem and the play. See the note in the Introduction on* The Code of Chivalry *(on page 54.)*

NINEVE	For these three days shake off your heavy load. When the time comes we'll set you on the road. Till then, I'm certain, 450 we shall prove good hosts. And learn from your own lips, I have no doubt, the language of courtesy and love.

(ARTHUR and GUINEVERE narrate.)

ARTHUR	Then the Lady and her servant took their leave, and Gawain and Bertilak remained alone.
GUINEVERE	And they drank more wine, and the night deepened, and they talked of many things . . .
ARTHUR	Until at last the Lord leaned forward in his chair . . .
GUINEVERE	And lightly placed his hand upon Gawain's arm and spoke.
BERTILAK	Tomorrow I go hunting. You'll stay here and rest. But I have 460 it in my mind for us to make a bargain. Nothing of any weight or importance. Call it . . . an entertainment, a pastime to suit this festive time of year. Let us agree that, whatever I may win upon the chase, it shall be yours, my gift to you. And, if you should chance, during the day, to win anything here, then, upon my return, that thing shall be mine, your gift to me. Well, Sir Gawain? Will you indulge me? Shall we make this bargain between us?
ARTHUR	And Gawain agreed. What else could he do?
GUINEVERE	The Lord was his host. And he was his guest. 470
ARTHUR	And what harm was there in it? A pastime, a fancy.
GUINEVERE	A Midwinter Game. There was no harm in it.
ARTHUR	And so he agreed.
GUINEVERE	He agreed to make the bargain.
ARTHUR	And Bertilak grasped his hand to make the bargain firm. And as he grasped his hand – as the Lord of the castle gripped the knight's hand and grinned – and as Gawain felt that hand's strength bite deep into his own . . .

SIR GAWAIN It was then that I knew this was no dream.

(MORGANA steps forward and speaks to the audience.)   480

MORGANA So far in this story we have seen
How Gawain,
The best of Arthur's knights,
Has taken up this fearful quest, and,
With strength of heart and hand,
Set forth on his journey through unknown, unmapped
   lands.
And we can't doubt his valour,
For he's fought with monsters and endured
Harsh storms,   490
All that the earth can conjure
To bring harm
He has survived, and when at last all seemed lost
Has faced without fear the prospect of his death,
His only thought turned heavenwards
To Christ and Holy Mary.
Surely we can say, without a doubt,
Of his kind he's the best,
The image of a very perfect, gentle knight.

And now, it seems, a miracle has occurred,   500
Waking from nightmare into dream
He finds himself here, in this place of seeming pleasure,
Guest of its gracious Lord and Lady,
Where he can take his ease and leisure,
As if it's some reward,
A happy interlude
Before he has to face his day of doom.
But is this all? Or is there more
Than meets the eye?
What subtle perils may there lie in store,   510
What secret traps and snares,
Might we find hidden here?
For what seems

Is not always what is.
And this goes for Gawain.
Is he all he appears?
What frailty does his courtliness conceal?
What weaknesses and faults
Lie at the core
Of this man's human heart?   520

We'll soon find out
For this, without a doubt,
It is my purpose, and my pleasure
To reveal.

Night's passed. Gawain's slept. Morning has come. Early,
Bertilak has risen, taken horses and hounds, and gone
hunting. Late, Gawain rises, dresses, and goes down into
the hall. Where he finds breakfast, and my Lady waiting
for him.

(NINEVE enters to GAWAIN.)   530

NINEVE	You slept well, I hope, Gawain?
SIR GAWAIN	Very well, Lady.
NINEVE	And now you're fully rested.
SIR GAWAIN	Yes, I am.
NINEVE	Nothing disturbed you as you slept?
SIR GAWAIN	I slept peacefully.
NINEVE	No sound awoke you?
SIR GAWAIN	I heard nothing.
NINEVE	You were troubled by no dreams?
SIR GAWAIN	No, my Lady, I had no dreams. 540
NINEVE	No dream of someone coming into your chamber? A figure slipping silently in through the door, and standing over you as you slept? She gazed down upon you, as the first light of

morning fell upon your face, and softly, and gently, she reached out her hand, and with the tips of her fingers touched your face . . .

SIR GAWAIN No, my Lady. I had no such dream. But if I had . . .

NINEVE If you had . . .

SIR GAWAIN My waking from it would have been a bitter one.

NINEVE And if you had found it not to be a dream – if you had   550
woken to see the woman herself standing there above
you . . . ?

SIR GAWAIN I would have thanked Christ and His Mother, the blessed
Virgin Mary, for the working of such a wondrous miracle.

NINEVE Even to find yourself a prisoner?

SIR GAWAIN You hold me as your prisoner?

NINEVE Yes, I do.

SIR GAWAIN Then I am most fortunate in being blessed with such a
gentle and gracious gaoler.

NINEVE You don't yearn for your freedom?   560

SIR GAWAIN Fate holds me in chains. How can a man escape his fate?

NINEVE By the paying of a ransom.

SIR GAWAIN My freedom has a price, then?

NINEVE All things have a price.

SIR GAWAIN And what is mine?

NINEVE A kiss. Surely such a noble, honourable and courteous
knight as Sir Gawain would grant a lady a kiss?

SIR GAWAIN I am your prisoner. You are my gaoler. If a kiss is your price,
you must take it.

NINEVE Then I will. And, with this single kiss, I release you. Go   570
now. You are free. Until tomorrow.

(She kisses GAWAIN as MORGANA narrates.)

MORGANA   And the kiss is given. And as it's given, Bertilak's hounds pull down a stag on the hillside, and an arrow from the Lord's bow pierces its heart.

(BERTILAK narrates.)

BERTILAK   It was fine hunting, and a fine beast I killed. A true king of animals. I winded him at first light and pursued him all day. All across the country he led me, through streams and pools, over crags and hills. Finally, as the sun was setting, my hounds had him at bay, and he turned to face them. Such courage he showed as they fought him! Such strength of heart as they attempted to pull him down! Yet he could not escape his fate, which was to die beneath my hand. Here are his antlers. As we agreed, they're yours, my gift to you.   580

(GAWAIN turns to BERTILAK.)

SIR GAWAIN   I thank you, Lord Bertilak.

BERTILAK   And what of you, Sir Gawain? Have you won anything during your day here? If you have, it must be given up, as we agreed.   590

SIR GAWAIN   What I've gained in this house, I give with good will. Here, take my winnings. I gained nothing else, and I give it freely.

BERTILAK   A kiss? Excellent. It's a fine trophy. But how and where did you win such a prize?

SIR GAWAIN   To tell you that was not in our agreement. I've given what I won. Expect nothing else.

BERTILAK   Well, then, I must be content. And I am. But shall we make the same agreement for tomorrow?

SIR GAWAIN   If that's your wish.   600

BERTILAK   It is.

SIR GAWAIN   Then I have no objection.

BERTILAK   Good. We'll say no more about it. Come, now. I'm hungry. Let's eat.

(MORGANA narrates.)

MORGANA   They eat and make merry, say goodnight, go to their beds. They sleep. Gawain sleeps. And he wakes in the morning to find my lord gone hunting, and my Lady once more there to greet him.

(NINEVE speaks to GAWAIN.)   610

NINEVE   I wonder if you are truly what you say.

SIR GAWAIN   My Lady?

NINEVE   Are you all that you appear to be?

SIR GAWAIN   I am Gawain, no more, no less.

NINEVE   Are you, though. Are you Sir Gawain?

SIR GAWAIN   You doubt me?

NINEVE   I do.

SIR GAWAIN   For what reason?

NINEVE   If you were Sir Gawain, you would not have offended me.

SIR GAWAIN   I would not knowingly offend you, my Lady, for all the   620
world. You must tell me how I have.

NINEVE   Sir Gawain would not need to be told.

SIR GAWAIN   If there's a fault in me, I apologise for it.

NINEVE   Your only fault is that of neglect. Yesterday I favoured you with a kiss. Today, you keep that favour from me.

SIR GAWAIN   Only for fear of causing offence.

NINEVE   There would be no offence. Even if you were to take it by force.

SIR GAWAIN	That's something I would never do.
NINEVE	What woman would resist you if you did? What woman would wish to? 630
SIR GAWAIN	What man of honour would take by force what is not rightly his?
NINEVE	I wish to talk of love, not honour, Sir Gawain.
SIR GAWAIN	You own that's my name, then.
NINEVE	Yes. I know you are Sir Gawain. And I tell you, that if I were the richest woman in the world, if I could have all that I desired, I'd desire nothing more than to have you as my lord and husband.
SIR GAWAIN	But, my Lady, you have a husband. 640
NINEVE	Yes. I have a husband. He rides out and hunts his prey. As I hunt mine here.
SIR GAWAIN	You have me at your mercy. There's nowhere for me to turn.
NINEVE	Then with this kiss, I'll wound you, and claim you as my prize.

(She kisses him as MORGANA narrates.)

MORGANA	And with that kiss she pierces his heart. And out in the middle of a forest, a wild boar screams and falls to its death on the dark earth. 650

(BERTILAK narrates.)

BERTILAK	I tracked it through the trees. Where they grew thickest it turned and took its stand. What a monster it was! Six of my hounds it killed, ripped them to shreds with its tusks. Their howls filled the forest. The leaves were splashed with their blood. I've never fought such a brave creature. But finally I brought it down, pierced it through with the point of my spear. These are its tusks. They're yours. Now, Sir Gawain, what do you have for me?

(GAWAIN speaks to BERTILAK.)   660

SIR GAWAIN   My prize is the same as yesterday's. This single kiss is my gift to you.

BERTILAK   Again! It seems you have good hunting in my house, Sir Gawain.

SIR GAWAIN   No, my Lord. You're wrong. I'm not the hunter here, but the hunted.

(MORGANA narrates.)

MORGANA   Once more they feast. Once more the bargain is made. And when the night grows deep, when the castle's in darkness, and Gawain sleeps, this time he dreams.   670

(GAWAIN narrates his dream.)

SIR GAWAIN   I'm standing in the ruins of some great hall. Roofless, broken walls, empty windows, fallen stones. Everything's lit clear and sharp by the moonlight. At first it seems I'm alone, then I become aware of a figure standing, far off, at the other end of the hall. It's a woman. She's under an archway, looking towards me, but I can't see her face. Her face is hidden. She raises a hand, beckoning, calling, and I walk towards her across the cracked flagstones. And now I know why I can't see her face. It's covered by a veil. But   680 now she's lifting her hands to the veil, she's drawing it back, and at that moment, something suddenly leaps out of the shadows. A creature, part-beast, part-man, humped on all fours, with the wicked, shrivelled vampire-face of a bat. It crouches beside her, snarling, and the woman pulls back her veil – and she has the same face.

(NINEVE speaks to GAWAIN.)

NINEVE   Are you afraid of death, Sir Gawain?

SIR GAWAIN   Of death? No, my Lady.

NINEVE   It holds no terror for you?   690

SIR GAWAIN	Why should it?
NINEVE	All who live fear to die.
SIR GAWAIN	Those who live in fear of death, also live in fear of life.
NINEVE	Proud words!
SIR GAWAIN	I meant to speak them with humility.
NINEVE	You spoke them like a fool! A vain fool! Like all of your kind. You talk of love, yet all you love is death. Death sits on your shoulders like an ape, and makes mockery of the world. Do you hate life so much?
SIR GAWAIN	No . . .
NINEVE	Then why are you so eager to lose it?
SIR GAWAIN	I'm not . . .
NINEVE	You ride from here to certain death tomorrow.
SIR GAWAIN	Nothing's certain . . .
NINEVE	Your death *is* if you go to that place.
SIR GAWAIN	Yet I must go.
NINEVE	Why?
SIR GAWAIN	For my honour's sake. I gave my word.
NINEVE	Do your word and your honour mean more to you than your life?
SIR GAWAIN	Yes.
NINEVE	More than my love for you?
SIR GAWAIN	Your love?
NINEVE	You are not blind, Sir Gawain. You know you have become dear to me . . .
SIR GAWAIN	And you, my Lady, are dear to me . . .

700

71

NINEVE	Then stay. Do not go. Remain here. Turn your back on death, and live – for me.	
SIR GAWAIN	My life would be nothing if I betrayed my trust.	
NINEVE	You're determined, then.	720
SIR GAWAIN	My path is set. I must follow it to the end.	
NINEVE	Then as this is to be our final parting, is there something you can give me, a keepsake, for me to remember you by?	
SIR GAWAIN	If I had anything of value it would be yours. But I have nothing to give.	
NINEVE	If I'm to receive nothing from you, you shall have something of mine. It's this. A belt of green silk. Here.	
SIR GAWAIN	No, my Lady . . .	
NINEVE	I insist . . .	
SIR GAWAIN	I can take nothing . . .	730
NINEVE	You refuse me?	
SIR GAWAIN	It's not . . . proper that I should receive any . . . gift, until I achieve my quest . . .	
NINEVE	These are excuses! Your reason's plain enough to me! You think this piece of silk is not worthy of you!	
SIR GAWAIN	No . . . !	
NINEVE	You think it has no value – yet if you knew its true worth you would not refuse it.	
SIR GAWAIN	As it is yours, my Lady, its worth and value to me are beyond all calculation . . .	740
NINEVE	No more of your fine words, Sir Gawain! Listen to me. I speak to you plainly. This belt has the power that, whoever wears it, they cannot be harmed by any man. No blow of sword, or spear, or axe can harm him. Do you understand now why I wish you to take it?	

SIR GAWAIN	Yes.
NINEVE	And you will take it. No word of objection! I am determined in this, as you are to seek out your doom.
SIR GAWAIN	If it is your wish . . .
NINEVE	It is my desire and my command.
SIR GAWAIN	Then I cannot refuse.
NINEVE	Tie it about your waist, beneath your tunic – like this. Now it can't be seen, and no one shall know you wear it. Except me. And no one shall know, Sir Gawain. Not even my Lord and husband. For its power to take effect, this gift must remain a secret. You will say nothing?
SIR GAWAIN	It seems I have no choice.
NINEVE	Now nothing remains but for us to take our leave. And this kiss I give you shall be my last.

750

(She kisses GAWAIN as MORGANA narrates.)

760

MORGANA	And down in the valley, on the banks of a stream, a hound clamps is teeth tight on a fox's throat, and the bloody rag of its body is tossed in the air.

(BERTILAK narrates.)

BERTILAK	Poor hunting it was for me today. A single fox! He took some killing, though. I roused him in a copse early this morning, and chased him through the day, over hedges, through tangled thickets. A tricky customer he was to be sure. Many a hunt before, I think, he has out-raced. But now he's run his last, and his pelt and brush are yours.

77

(GAWAIN speaks to BERTILAK.)

SIR GAWAIN	As this single kiss is yours, according to our bargain.
BERTILAK	Your prize again? I thank you for it. But is this all you won today?

SIR GAWAIN	It is, my Lord.
BERTILAK	You had no other prize?
SIR GAWAIN	No other.
BERTILAK	A single kiss, and nothing more?
SIR GAWAIN	Nothing.
BERTILAK	So, our contract's at an end. As is your stay here with us. 780 Tomorrow you go on your way. To the Green Chapel. If you're still set on making that journey.
SIR GAWAIN	I am.
BERTILAK	There's nothing more to be said, then. We'll go now and have our last meal together.
SIR GAWAIN	I beg your leave to abstain. Tonight I mean to fast and pray, and leave here with the sun's rising.
BERTILAK	If that's your wish. I'll say goodnight, then, and goodbye.
SIR GAWAIN	I thank you. And I thank you too for your kindness and hospitality. 790
BERTILAK	It has been my fortune to have as guest a man of such nobility and courtesy, such honesty and honour. I truly hope and pray that all goes well with you. And that God stands by you in your coming ordeal.

(MORGANA and NINEVE narrate.)

MORGANA/ **NINEVE**	Then the lord takes his final leave of the knight And the knight goes to the chapel to pray. He kneels on the floor where the moon shines bright And shrives his soul for the coming day.
	But the prayer in his throat is solid stone 800 His thoughts are heavy as iron weights And the devil's own cold strips them down to the bone And holds them fast from heaven's gates.

All night he struggles to climb to grace
And cleanse his spirit in heaven's light
But all he sees is the Lady's face
As the belt at his waist begins to bite.

Then he gives up his mind to the dark's deep
And slowly he falls to the stony floor
And sinks into sleep as all the stars weep   810
Bitter tears – for heaven has closed its doors.

(ARTHUR and GUINEVERE narrate.)

ARTHUR	The night passed. Morning came.
GUINEVERE	New Year's morning, heavy with cloud.
ARTHUR	He woke. He could feel the cold wind on his skin.
GUINEVERE	He was lying on the earth. The castle had gone.
ARTHUR	He was on the hilltop he'd come to three days before.
GUINEVERE	And everything was as it had been three days before.
ARTHUR	Except that, where the stones had been . . .
GUINEVERE	Where that circle of broken stones had stood . . . 820
ARTHUR	There now stood a mound . . .
GUINEVERE	A grass-covered mound, like some burial chamber . . .
ARTHUR	And like a man in a dream . . .
GUINEVERE	Like a man who doesn't know whether he's awake or dreaming . . .
ARTHUR	A man who isn't sure anymore what is dream and what is real . . .
GUINEVERE	Gawain rose and walked towards it.
SIR GAWAIN	It was smooth and round. Perfectly formed. Man-made, no mere creation of nature. And when I placed my hand on it, 830 it was warm. As if it was a living thing. I looked for an

entrance but there was none. No entrance or doorway anywhere. Only the smooth, green, warm sides of the mound. But I knew it was here for a purpose, and I knew that if I waited, that purpose would be revealed.

ARTHUR Then he heard a sound.

GUINEVERE A sound coming from within.

ARTHUR A grinding, a scraping, as of stone against steel.

GUINEVERE The sound of a blade being sharpened.

ARTHUR And this sound grew louder and the mound trembled . . . 840

GUINEVERE It trembled and shook and split open . . .

ARTHUR Earth and rock burst wide . . .

GUINEVERE And where there had been no doorway . . .

ARTHUR Now there was a doorway . . .

GUINEVERE A dark doorway of earth and rock . . .

ARTHUR And out of that dark doorway . . .

GUINEVERE Axe in hand, stepped the Green Knight.

(BERTILAK and NINEVE bring on the GREEN KNIGHT.)

GREEN KNIGHT Sir Gawain! You're welcome here. You've come, I trust, to keep our tryst? 850

SIR GAWAIN Did you doubt I would?

GREEN KNIGHT Never. You're an honest man, I know.

SIR GAWAIN Well, then. Here I am

GREEN KNIGHT And here we are, alone. And ready for the next move in our game. The first was yours. The second, as we agreed, is mine.

SIR GAWAIN As we agreed.

GREEN KNIGHT Here's my axe. The blade's been newly sharpened.

SIR GAWAIN	Allow me, then, to test its edge.
GREEN KNIGHT	With your neck, you will. Step forward, so that I may strike. 860
SIR GAWAIN	I'm ready.
GREEN KNIGHT	You'll offer no resistance?
SIR GAWAIN	I'll stand unarmed and take your blow.
GREEN KNIGHT	Your neck bared to the axe without protection?
SIR GAWAIN	Only my courage and faith in Christ.
GREEN KNIGHT	Only that and nothing more?
SIR GAWAIN	Only that.
GREEN KNIGHT	Prepare yourself, then.
SIR GAWAIN	I'm prepared.
GREEN KNIGHT	You're trembling. 870
SIR GAWAIN	It's the cold, nothing more. My heart's firm. Strike now when you will. But a single blow, only.
GREEN KNIGHT	A single blow, as we agreed. A single blow is all I'll need.

(ARTHUR and GUINEVERE narrate.)

ARTHUR	Then the giant took his stance . . .
GUINEVERE	And prepared to strike . . .
ARTHUR	He lifted his axe . . .
GUINEVERE	Raised it high in the air . . .
ARTHUR	And for a brief moment . . . 880
GUINEVERE	He held it there . . .
ARTHUR	And then . . .
GUINEVERE	And then . . .

(GAWAIN now turns and narrates to ARTHUR and GUINEVERE, as if he is back at Camelot, relating the story of what happened.)

SIR GAWAIN   And then he brought it down. I heard the whistle of the blade, I saw the flash of the metal. But it moved slowly through the air, as if the air had become water, and the water was slowly freezing to ice. And it seemed that for an age I stood there, watching as the axe came falling   890 towards me.

ARTHUR   And then?

GUINEVERE   And then?

SIR GAWAIN   And then, at the very moment the blade touched my neck, at the instant it broke the skin and cut into the flesh and drew first blood – at that very moment, it stopped.

ARTHUR   The axe stopped?

SIR GAWAIN   It stopped, frozen. He stood, frozen.

GUINEVERE   And you were unharmed?

SIR GAWAIN   Except for the smallest cut, yes.   900

ARTHUR   Another wonder!

GUINEVERE   A wonder to outmatch all the others.

SIR GAWAIN   I thought so too. But there was a greater yet wonder to come.

ARTHUR   Tell us of it, Gawain.

GUINEVERE   Tell us of this new wonder.

SIR GAWAIN   There was the Green Knight, frozen on the hilltop, as if time had stopped. And there, coming towards me, down from the crest of the hill, a figure. As soon as I saw her I knew her. It was the old woman from the castle, the Lady's   910 servant. But now her face was fierce and proud, and she fixed me with her gaze – but it was to the Green Knight she first spoke.

(MORGANA speaks to the GREEN KNIGHT.)

MORGANA Go now. Return. Your work here is done.

(BERTILAK and NINEVE take the GREEN KNIGHT away.)

SIR GAWAIN And he turned away and walked back into the mound, and it closed behind him as if he had never been. Then the old woman . . .

ARTHUR Yes! The old woman! 920

GUINEVERE Who was this old woman?

ARTHUR Did she tell you who she was?

GUINEVERE Did she tell you her name?

ARTHUR Yes. When I asked her, she told me her name.

(MORGANA speaks to GAWAIN.)

MORGANA I am Morgana.

ARTHUR Morgana! The Witch!

MORGANA The goddess.

GUINEVERE So she calls herself.

MORGANA I am as I am. This is my domain you have come to, man, 930
more ancient than yours. And it is my power that has
brought you here – and that power too is more ancient
than yours.

ARTHUR Then everything was all her doing?

GUINEVERE I feared it might be. I felt her hand in this.

MORGANA All my doing, Gawain. All the creatures you have
encountered – the Lord and his Lady, the Green Knight – all
are my creations, all fashioned to my single purpose.

ARTHUR Her purpose? It could be none that was good.

GUINEVERE Her nature is bent towards the making of mischief. Tell us. 940
What was her purpose?

MORGANA My purpose, Gawain,
Is to show you, man,
The thing that you are.
Not the shine and the show,
But the true thing below
That which appears so fair.
Not what seems,
But what is.
Not the glitter and the gloss   950
Of glory and fame,
Honour, nobility, and all the rest
Of those high-sounding names,
But the worm
In the fruit,
The crack in the shining, armoured suit,
The human flaw in your human heart,
Your dishonour and dishonesty,
Your betrayal and your treachery
And your shame.   960

ARTHUR What did she mean?

GUINEVERE What treachery and shame?

MORGANA A gift that was taken . . .
A bargain that was broken . . .
A betrayal of trust . . .
That belt at your waist.

SIR GAWAIN And her words cut through me, wounded me deeper than
any sword or axe. I understood at last the trap she'd set for
me, and into which I'd walked, blind to my own weakness
and failing. This belt that I'd kept for fear of my life – this   970
belt with which I'd tried to cheat death of its right – this
belt for the keeping of which I'd broken my word – I wore
now as the mark of my shame – revealing me for what I am
– my whole life a sham – no perfect knight but flawed and
fallen man.

MORGANA	And as you fall So shall you all The worm in your heart Shall eat its way out And bring to an end 980 This kingdom of men That will pass at the last To the dark and the dust And the land shall be brought To the day of its fate And there shall be darkness, despair and defeat Through betrayal and treachery and shame and deceit.
ARTHUR	And, as in a vision, we saw the end of things as they would come to pass . . .
GUINEVERE	A king betrayed, a queen disgraced . . . 990
ARTHUR	Factions split, the kingdom divided . . .
GUINEVERE	The sword shattered, the bright crown broken . . .
BERTILAK	And where there had been order, chaos and confusion . . .
NINEVE	And where there had been peace, discord and strife . . .
ARTHUR	Brother against brother . . .
GUINEVERE	Son against father . . .
BERTILAK	And the drum of doom bringing the clash of battle . . .
NINEVE	And the country filled with the sounds of slaughter . . .
ARTHUR	And after the slaughter, silence . . .
GUINEVERE	Silence, in which the eye stared blind . . . 1000
BERTILAK	Silence, where the tongue lay stilled in the mouth . . .

we saw the end of things . . . *The lines that follow describe the end of Arthur's Golden Age, which was brought about by Guinevere's betrayal of Arthur with Lancelot, and the treachery of Arthur's illegitimate son, Mordred.*

NINEVE   Silence, where the wheel lay broken in the mud . . .

ARTHUR   And the child lay silent in the cold womb . . .

GUINEVERE   And the mist lay silent upon the Black Lake . . .

BERTILAK   And all that had been passed into the mist and the silence . . .

NINEVE   And when the mist cleared, and the lake was empty of all but silence . . .

MORGANA   And after the silence – soft laughter.

(The PLAYERS now speak again as themselves, and as they 1010 *speak, they take off the costume they have been wearing, and place them, along with the props, back on the cart.)*

1st PLAYER   And so it was that Gawain returned to Camelot, and made known there all that had befallen him in his quest.

2nd PLAYER   And all who heard were wondrous of it, and some shook their heads, and to many it was a mystery not to be fathomed.

3rd PLAYER   As it was a mystery to us, who had dreamed it, and woken, and found that dream still clear in our memories.

4th PLAYER   And remaining clear as we went back to the road, travelling 1020 through hard country and hard times.

5th PLAYER   And often we felt the heaviness of the sky above us, and the heaviness of the earth beneath us, and saw the cold rain falling, and felt the cold wind blowing.

The Black Lake *After the final battle which saw the destruction of Arthur's kingdom, Arthur, mortally wounded, was taken on a barge by 12 women across the waters of a lake to the Isle of Avalon, and never seen again. There is a tradition that he and his knights are sleeping in some hidden place, waiting for a time when their power is needed again, and they will wake and ride forth once more. Several caves and hills across Britain claim to be the resting-place of Arthur and his knights. The Isle of Avalon is supposedly located at Glastonbury in Somerset, where there was once a lake.*

6th PLAYER   And we thought how the world had been, and how it was, and wept for that dream and for that vanished kingdom.

1st PLAYER   As Gawain wept, living to see it pass, before he passed himself into the mist and the darkness.

2nd PLAYER   As all things must pass into the mist and the darkness.

3rd PLAYER   But as long as their memory remains something of them   1030
lives on.

4th PLAYER   The memory which is the dream that we carry with us.

5th PLAYER   And lives on in the stories we make of those dreams.

6th PLAYER   And such is our story, and this is the play we have made of it.

(The PLAYERS make their bows to the audience, then they go, taking the cart and all their belongings with them, and leaving the stage empty.)

(The end.)

before he passed himself into the darkness *Gawain was killed fighting in a battle against Lancelot, just before the battle in which Arthur was mortally wounded fighting against Mordred.*

DISCUSSION The play is performed by 'poor players' travelling on the road, who carry their props and costumes with them.

In small groups, discuss what props and costumes you think they would be carrying, that would be useful in performing *Sir Gawain and the Green Knight*. Both costumes and props need to be simple and basic – the kinds of items that could be carried and used quite easily – but also effective.

Make a list of your props and costumes, and discuss with other groups what you've chosen, and why.

FINDING OUT The poem was written in the Middle Ages, towards the end of the 14th Century. See what you can find out about some of the important events that took place in England between 1380 and 1400. Also see what you can find out about the everyday lives of the people of those times.

WRITING/ARTWORK It is suggested that the Green Knight is some kind of large figure or puppet, carried by two of the players, who also speak his lines. How would you create such a figure, and what would it look like?

Either write a brief description of your idea of how the Green Knight would be created, or make a sketch, showing how it would be used in a performance. Remember that simplicity and effectiveness are both of equal importance.

If you have a different idea of how to create the Green Knight on stage, write a brief description of this.

ACTING In the play, there's a constant mix of narrative and action, with characters switching quickly between speaking to the audience and to each other. In small groups, find a short section of the play where this happens, and try acting it out.

Afterwards, discuss what you think worked and what didn't. Try acting out the scene several times in different ways, until you find the way you think works best.

Perhaps you could then improvise the same scene, using your own words, and without any narration. Then, afterwards, discuss the differences between the two.

DISCUSSION A key moment in the first part of the play, is when the Green Knight's head is struck off, and it continues to speak.

As a class, discuss different ways in which this scene could be staged for a performance. When you're discussing this, bear in mind the effect you want this scene to have on the audience.

WRITING Gawain has several adventures during his journey north. Take one of the adventures mentioned in the play, and write about it in more detail, either as a poem or a short story – in the third person, or as if Gawain himself was speaking.

LANGUAGE Below is an extract from the poem, *Sir Gawain and the Green Knight*, followed by a translation into modern English. It's from the section that describes Gawain's journey.

Mony klyf he ouerclambe in contrayez straunge,	Many a cliff he climbed o'er in countries unknown,
Fer floten fro his frendez fremedly he rydez.	far fled from his friends without fellowship he rode.
At vche warpe oper water per pe wyze passed	At every wading or water on the way that he passed
He fonde a foo hym byfore, bot ferly hit were,	he found a foe before him, save at few for a wonder;
And pat so foule and so felle pat fezt hym byhode.	and so foul were they and fell that fight he must needs.
So mony meruayl bi mount per pe mon fyndez,	So many a marvel in the mountains he met in those lands
Hit were to tore for to telle of pe tenpe dole.	that 'twould be tedious the tenth part to tell you thereof.
Sumwhyle wyth wormez he werrez, and with wolues als,	At whiles with worms he wars, and with wolves also,
Sumwhyle wyth wodwos, pat woned in pe knarrez,	at whiles with wood-trolls that wandered in the crags,
Bope wyth bullez and berez, and borez operquyle,	and with bulls and with bears and with boars, too, at times;
And etaynez, pat hym anelede of pe heze felle;	and with ogres that hounded him from the heights of the fells.

(Translation by J.R.R. Tolkien, published by Unwin, 1975)

The language the poem is written in was the dialect spoken at the time in the north-west Midlands, and is a form of early English! Go through the section, and make a list of all those words you recognise and understand.

Now make a list of the words (and even letters!) you don't recognise or understand. Using the translation, write down what these words mean in modern English, perhaps using a table like the one here.

Word/Letter	Meaning
floten	fled
ouerclambe	climbed over
p	th
wodwo	wood-troll

The poem uses alliteration and blank verse. Alliteration is when several words grouped together begin with, or contain the same letter or sound. Blank verse is verse where the ends of the lines do not rhyme. Go through the section, and find examples of alliteration.

Look at the same section in the play, and see if you can find moments where the playwright also uses alliteration.

DISCUSSION Morgana tells Gawain that her purpose was to uncover Gawain's human weaknesses, to reveal his 'dishonesty, betrayal and treachery'.

As a class, discuss how you think Gawain has been dishonest and treacherous, and why he finds this so shameful.

WRITING How would you describe Gawain? What kind of person is he? Do you think he's changed by the events of the play? Make notes on his character, and use these notes to write a short essay about him, and how you think the events of the play might have changed him.

ARTWORK Design a poster for a performance of *Sir Gawain and the Green Knight*.

READING There are many versions of stories about King Arthur and his knights. There are bound to be several in your local or school library. Find one of these, and read some of the stories.

You might also want to read one or two of the poems in *The Idylls of the King*, written by the Victorian poet, Alfred, Lord Tennyson.

Also, try reading a translation in modern English of *The Wife of Bath's Tale* from *The Canterbury Tales* by Geoffrey Chaucer. *The Canterbury Tales* were written around the same time as *Sir Gawain and the Green Knight*. *The Wife of Bath's Tale* is a version of another Gawain story.

There are also modern novels that draw heavily upon the Arthur myth, such as *The Weirdstone of Brisingamen* by Alan Garner, and Susan Cooper's sequence of five novels, *The Dark Is Rising*. The first two of these novels, *Over Sea, Under Stone* and *The Dark Is Rising* were dramatised on radio by David Calcutt.

LOOKING BACK AT THE PLAYS

1 DISCUSSION: CASTING THE MAJOR ROLES

In pairs, discuss which film or television actors you would cast in each of the major roles in the three plays, noting down brief reasons to support your choices. Compare your ideas in a class discussion.

2 DISCUSSION: COMPARING THE THREE PLAYS

What do the three plays have in common, in terms of their subject-matter and the styles in which they are written? Discuss as a class which one you like most and explain why.

3 NOTE-MAKING AND DISCUSSION: ENGLAND IN THE MIDDLE AGES

In pairs, look back through the three plays and note down what impression they give of England in the Middle Ages. What kinds of stories did people tell? What was the importance of drama? What were people afraid of? What did they believe in?

4 WRITING: NEWSPAPER ARTICLES

How would a newspaper from the Middle Ages have reported on the events portrayed in these plays? Write either (i) a front-page report on the mysterious deaths in Dicing with Death; or (ii) a theatre review of the performance of the mystery play which took place some weeks later than the rehearsals depicted; or (iii) a report of the strange events in Arthur's castle at the beginning of *Sir Gawain and the Green Knight*.

5 ARTWORK: DESIGNING A POSTER

Work in pairs on a poster to advertise a stage performance of one of the three plays. First discuss as a class the words and images that usually appear on posters of this kind.

6 ARTWORK AND WRITING: A THEATRE PROGRAMME

Create a programme for a production of the three plays as a 'triple bill' in the theatre. Remember to include the cast that you have decided upon, as well as introductory articles on the three stories and historical background on features of the Middle Ages such as mystery plays, the Black Death and the King Arthur stories.